NUMBER 44

THE ENGLISH EXPERIENCE

ITS RECORD IN EARLY PRINTED BOOKS
PUBLISHED IN FACSIMILE

WILLIAM CUNINGHAM

THE COSMOGRAPHICAL GLASSE

LONDON 1559

DA CAPO PRESS
THEATRVM ORBIS TERRARVM LTD.
AMSTERDAM 1968 NEW YORK

The publishers acknowledge their gratitude
to the Trustees of the Bodleian Library, Oxford,
for their permission to reproduce
the Library's copy.

S.T.C. No. 6119
Collation: A-S^6, T^4.
With one folding plate.

Published in 1968 by
Theatrum Orbis Terrarum Ltd.,
O.Z. Voorburgwal 85, Amsterdam
&
Da Capo Press
- a division of Plenum Publishing Corporation -
227 West 17th Street, New York. 10011
Library of Congress Catalog Card Number:

68 — 54632
Printed in The Netherlands

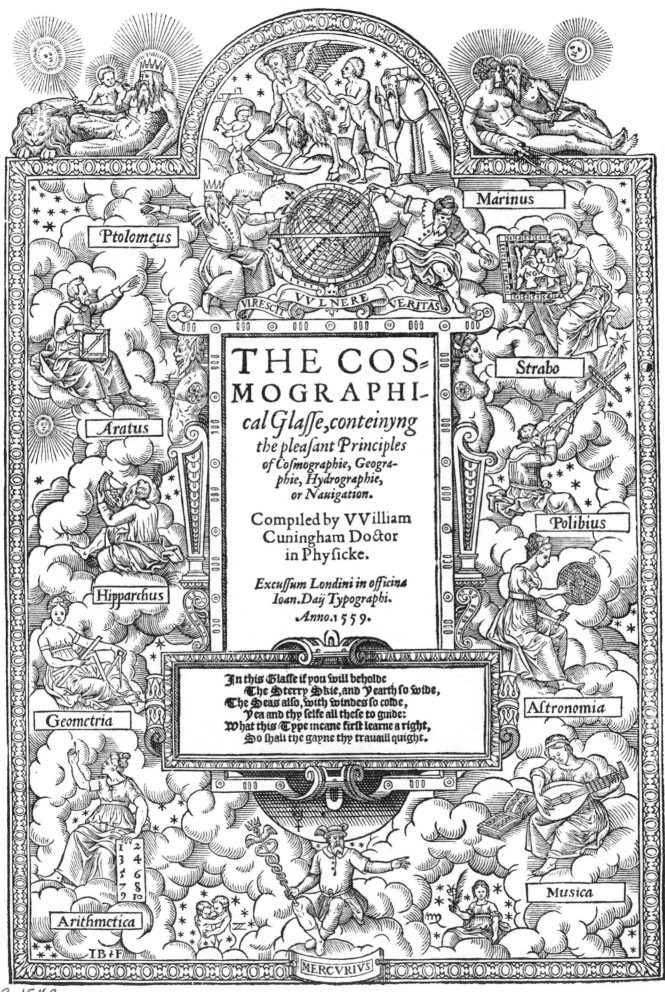

THE COS=
MOGRAPHI-
cal Glaſſe, conteinyng
the pleaſant Principles
of Coſmographie, Geogra-
phie, Hydrographie,
or Nauigation.

Compiled by VVilliam
Cuningham Doctor
in Phyſicke.

Excuſſum Londini in officina
Ioan. Daÿ Typographi.
Anno. 1559.

In this Glaſſe if you will beholde
The Sterry Skie, and Yearth ſo wide,
The Seas also, with windes ſo colde,
Yea and thy ſelfe all theſe to guide:
What this Type meane firſt learne a right,
So ſhall the gayne thy trauaill quight.

Ptolomeus

Marinus

Strabo

Aratus

Polibius

Hipparchus

Astronomia

Geometria

Musica

Arithmetica

VIRESCIT VVLNERE VERITAS

MERCVRIVS

IB·F

✣ TO THE RIGHT HONORA-
ble the Lorde Robert Duddeley, of the mooſte
noble Order of the Garter Knight , Maiſter of the
Horſe, to the Quenes mooſt excellente Maieſtye:
and his ſinguler good Lorde, and
Maiſter. &c.

ÆDALVS THAT EX-
cellent Geometrician (right ho-
norable) whan as with the eyes
of knowledge , he did beholde
that horrible Mõſter Ignorãce,
he therwith præſently concei-
ued ſuche intollarable griefe,
that he daily ſought occaſion e-
ther how to baniſh hir his præ-
ſence and companye : or els by
what meanes to eſcape , oute of
her lothſome Labyrinthe . At
lengthe, perceiuinge ſhe coulde
not be baniſhed , he præpared
winges (throughe Science aide) and ſo did flye oute of hir mooſte filthy Priſon : according to the pleaſant Poëte.

Dædalus fabrifaſtis alis Cœlum ipſum adiuit.

He made him winges wherwith to flie:
Aſcending to the Sterrye Skie.

Yea this Monſter haue in all ages bene accompted ſo deformed and
Vile, that thoſe whoſe companye ſhe frequented, were reputed not in
the numbre of reaſonable Creatures : but of brute beaſtes. For what
doth man differ from a beaſt in nature, if he (leauing reaſons rule) folowe his ſenſuall appetite as they do ? Or wherein dothe he ſo neare
approche vnto God in likeneſſe : as by Science, and Knowledge ? for
this thing is proper to God only , to know all thinges : and vnto beaſt
to be in all things ignorant, except in ſuch as ther ſenſes and cuſtome
teach them. VVhich hathe ingendred ſuch immortall hate towardes
this lothſome wight, leaſt man ſhould loſe his name and dignity, that
he inuented all Artes, ſought out all Secretes, and laboured throughe
curiouſe workes, to bring her into perpetuall exile. But nowe in theſe
daies, leſt ſhe ſhould returne againe (admoniſhed by theſe examples)
I though one of leaſte ſtrengthe and force, yet not of leaſt good will,
haue deuiſed this mirrour, or Coſmographical Glaſſe. In which, mē
may behold not one or two perſonages, but the heauens with her planets and ſtarres , th'Earthe with her beautifull Regions, and the Seas
with her merueilous increſe. So that ſhe ſhal not (if men be diligent)
creape into anye of theſe places , withoute eſpyeng. Yet conſidering

with my felf, howe that Ignoraunce hath left no fmall number of her
frendes among vs, which feke to deface both fcience and her feruants,
I haue no other refuge to kepe this my Glaffe from perifhing, then to
be an humble futer vnto your honoure (which doth not only fauour
Science, but alfo haue geuen her within your breaft a reaftinge place)
that it may come forth vnder your noble protection: and be defended
as Teucer was vnder the fhield of mighty Aiax, againft two fortes of
men especially. Of which, th'one will difpraife and defpife fuch thinges as they neuer red, and are vtterly ignorante in. The other forte
will of mere arrogácy il report al mens trauailes, how exacte and perfite fo euer they be, they them felues (like Draens) remaininge withoute profite.   As for the learned, wife, and modeft, I am fure will not
rafhly geue fentence: but if faultes efcape, eyther frendly admonifhe:
or els with penne fpedely amende it, vnto whiche fute I am the more
bouldened, remembring as well your excellent vertues, and giftes of
nature, whiche for feare of fufpicion of flatterye I ouerpaffe, as to all
men euident: as alfo your Lordfhippes incoragement of me to knowledge, bothe in wordes and mooft liberall rewardes. VVherefore, if
it fhall pleafe your honore to take this fimple worke into your tuiti-
on, and be Patrone vnto it: I fhall be bouldened (God grauntinge
life) to prefente you alfo wyth other of my laboures, the Titles of
whiche foloweth.

1	*An Apologie*	*Lib.ij.*
2	*A new Quadrat, of no man euer publifhed.*	*Lib.ij.*
3	*The Aftronomicall Ring.*	*Lib.ij*
4	*Organographia.*	*Lib.iij*
5	*Gazophilacion Aftronomicum.*	*Lib.xvj*
6	*Chronographia.*	*Lib.xij*
7	*Comentaries in Hippocrates de Aëre, Aquis, & Re- gionibus.*	*Lib.iij*

VVith diuers others, whofe names I omit for fondry caufes. Thus I
leaue at this prefente, to trouble your honor with my rude Letters,
prayeng God to graunt you long life, continuall helth, increafe of honor: and after this life, a place of Ioy, and comfort.

Your Lordfhippes mooft humble Seruaunt,

VV. Cuningham Phyfition.

Gilberti Barcklei Grimbienſ. ſacræ Theologiæ
Profeſſ. in Speculum Coſmographicum
Ὀγδοάστιχον.

Machina conſpicui variis pulcherrima mundi
    Digna modis homini cognitione venit.
Mira Creatoris patet hinc Sapientia, Virtus,
    Et Bonitas, cui ſit ſemper habendus honos.
Quod grauis Ægyptus, quod Athenis Græcia rerum,
    Quod docuit Muſis æmula Roma ſuis:
Hocce Cuninghamus ſtudijs Gulielmus acutis
    Anglus in hoc libro Nordouicenſis agit.

Th. mæ Langlei Cantabrigienſis ad
Lectorem Carmen.

Si totam toto diuiſus ab orbe Britannus
    Noſcere Tellurem, ſi Mare percupiat,
Climata, quinquè Plagas, Circlos, poſituſque Locorum,
    Sydereos curſus, Tropica Signa, Polos,
Quæquè Dies tenebris æquant, quæ tempora mutant,
    Lumine cur Phœbus, Lunaquè deficiant,
Gadibus occiduis ater quàm diſſidet Indus,
    Et quantum diſtent à Scythe, Maurus, Arabs,
Spacia metiri, terras deſcribere, & vrbes
    Præſtantes charta pingere in exigua,
Nomina ventorum, Claſſes maria omnia circum
    Ducere, & ad portum quamquè, referre ſuum,
Qui quibus Ἀντίποδες, Ἀντοικοι, quiqȝe Περίοικοι,
    Vmbras qui varient: hæc docet iſte liber.
En Strabo, Sollinus, Plinius, Mela, & Ptolomæus,
    Libris ac tabulis quæ docuere ſuis,
Vnus cuncta tibi monſtrat liber iſte legenti:
    Ære potes paruo, diſcere multa breui.
Hæc Cuninghamus ſparſim diffuſa coëgit
    Sedulus inſtar apis, quò tibi proſit Opus.
Effecit & primus, vt Κοσμογραφία noſtras
    Effingat voces: Momus hic eſſe caue.

Dyſtichon eiuſdem.

Hic mundi tractus, terras, Mare, Sidera, Ventos,
    Vmbras, atquè ſitus, ſpacia quanta, ſcies.

Authoris Δύστιχον.

Vis Terræ Tractus? Pelagi vis noſcere fluxus?
    Hoc tibi deſcripſi (candide lector) opus.

❧ THE PRÆFACE OF THE
Author, setting out the dignitie, and Ample vse of Cosmographie.

IF EVER THERE wer Art for all mēs vse inuen=ted, Science set forth wherein consisteth Sapience, or Trea-sure worthy to be had in esti-mation: no doughte (louynge Reader)either Cosmographie is the same,or els it is not to be founde vppon th'Earth.For if we do well consider with oure selues what her office is, there is no man I suppose ,so meane witted,but will confesse her ample vse,nor yet so simply learned but must acknowledge her manifold benefites.And if I shall begin with the defence of our Coūtry,which ought to be more præcious,thē Pa-rentes wife Children or Consanguinitie, Cosmographie herein do so much profite,that without it both valeaunt Corage,Policy and Pui=saunce oftentimes can take no place. For by her we are taught whi=che way to conduct most safely our ooste,where to pitch oure tentes, where to winter:yea,and where most aptlye to encounter with them in the fielde.VVhich thing Alexander the mighty Conqueroure vn-derstanding,accustomed to haue the Mappe and Carte of the Coun-try,by his Cosmographers set out,with which he would warre.Com-maunding it also to be hanged in open markets for all men to behold, wherby the Capitaines did forsee,and seke out where was the easiest places to arriue,and the Souldiors allured with the commodities of the Countries,were made the willinger to the thinge.This was it which gat him so many victories,and made him so great à Cōqueror. This was it which obteined the Romanes their fame,more then ther force and strength.This hathe bene to all men profitable,and iniuri=ous to no man.On the contrarye parte,what domage,yea vtter sub=uertion hathe folowed to moste noble Princes,and valeaunte Capi-taines throughe Ignorance of this Art,histories full well can testify.

And that amonge manye, I maye resight one Example, was not the
mightye pertian King Cyrus (who had brought Babilon, and all the
East partes in subiection) vanquished withall his armye of Tomyris
the Scythiã Quene, at the Riuer Oäxis, as he shuld haue passed ouer?
what shall I speake of Agamemnons armye in the Troian warres: of
the Persians, against the Leonidians: or of Crassus, against the Par=
theans: whiche ware them selues destroyed, or made captiue, theyr
wiues children and family spoyled, and theyr country most ruinously
subuerted, for want of Cosmographie. Also, as touching the study of
diuinitie, it is so requisite, and neadfull, that you shall not vnderstãd
any boke, ether of th'old law or Prophets (yea I had almost said, any
part of à booke, or Chapter of the same) being in this Art ignoraunt.
For what numbre of places, Ilands, Regions, Cities, Townes, Moun=
tains, Seas, Riuers, and such like, is ther to be found in euery Booke?
How often doth father Moses in his.v.bookes, make mention of Ba=
bilon, Sinehar, Armenia (in whose hilles, Noë his Arke stayed after
the vniuersal deludge) Assur, Charan, Caphdorim or Caldæa, Ægipt
called of the Hebrues Mizraim, Syria (deuided into thre parts, Me=
sopotamia, Arabia, and Æthiopia,) with infinite like places, whiche
without Cosmographie can nether be rightly vnderstand, or yet tru=
lye expounded? VVhat contention, and strife, haue ther spronge in all
ages amonge th'Interpreters of the scriptures, touching the situatiõ
of Paradice: their owne workes moste euidentlye beare witnesse. All
they agree in this poynt, that it is à place of ioy, reast, and abounding
in all kinde of pleasures, but yet as touchinge the situation, some vn=
derstand it spiritually: some imagin it ether in heauen or in the harts
of the quiet and faithfull: other affirme it à place in th'Earth at this
præsent yet remaining, but is so kepte with Angels that no man maye
come to it: some say it is in th'East part of the worlde, aboue the mid=
dle reagion of th'Aëre, and so is free from the violence of all windes.
Other suppose it to be in the burning Zone, vnder th'Equinoctiall:
So that not two in this poynt do accord. But yet of all the rest, ther o=
pinions semeth most fond, whiche place it in the middle region of the
Aëre, and also those, that vnderstand it spiritually, for that the scrip=
ture affirmeth it to be in th'Earth, and the.iiij famous floudes (Eu=
phrates, Hidekel nowe called Tigris, Gihon, which many interprete
Nilus, and Phison at this daye named Ganges (to come from thence.
These

These thinges I bring in only as example, to proue the necessarye vse
of it in deuinitie, and not to dispute ether of Paradise or his situatiō,
seing it belongeth not to my profession, and office. Moreouer mannes
helth (withoute whiche Honour, Fame, Richesse, Frendes, and Life
it selfe, semeth bothe troublous, and noysome) can not be conserued in
perfite estate, or once lost be recouered and restored without Cosmographie. For howe greatlye herein it profiteth, to consider the temperature of Regions, Cities, and Townes, in what Zone, & vnder what
Clymate and Parallele they are situated: Hippocrates dothe plainlye
set out. Yea it might seme superfluous, to show how bothe he & Galenus, commaunded ther pacients to remoue from one place, to an other
(especiallye in longe sickenesse) because of th'alteration of th'Aëre.
VVhat it auaileth also, to know the natures of waters, the quality &
pertition of windes, the maners & complexions of th'inhabitantes all
Physicions right well do vnderstand. And to cōclude, in th'election of
simples, as stones, treis, rotes, herbes, gummes, earthes, metals, beasts,
foules, & fishes, what lighte springeth by consideringe the countrye
from whence they are brought: I suppose no man of that profession, is
ignorant. In the making, & ordaining lawes, for brideling mans fro-
ward appetide, Cosmographie is not vnfrutfull. For she setteth out the
natures of all people, the lawes and statutes by which they are gouerned, & the sequele of euery decre established. Grammarians also, can
not fullye vnderstande the pleasaunt inuention & perfite sence of the
witty Poëtes, but by Cosmographies aide, because of the names of Regions, Cities, Townes, waters, fluddes, mountaines, ceremonies, people
and monsters, which euery Poet do commenlye introduce, in all theyr
writinges. I omit for breuitie, th'incredible benefits, whiche springe
by reading of Histories: the beautye, & ornature of which, consisteth
in the description of countreis, names of people, & nature of th'inhabitants: whiche remaine as vnknowne of th'inexperte of Cosmogra-
ghie. Moreouer, the famous marchaunts, haue by it not onlye inriched
them selues, but also their country: fineding out suche commodities, as
without it shuld remaine, as not knowne. Yea & that is daily more &
more perceiued, for what countrie, or Iland, is not in oure age sear-
ched out? what shall I herein speake of Vesputius Americus, who (by
his knowledge in Cosmographie) found out America, the.iiij.parte of
the world, (vnknowne in all ages before our time) to the great benefites

fites of all Europe. I may feme to vtter that all men know, in making
reherfall of th'Indians , Calicute, Ginea, the. v. Ilandes Moluccæ, alfo
Porne, Sololi, & infinite other, which are the frutes of Cofmographie
in this our age. Mariners & trauailers on the feas (without which no
realme can long ftand, or mans life be fuftaind) are bound to acknow=
ledge Cofmographies benefites. For it fetteth forthe there portes , it
fheweth ther courfe, it declareth th'ordre of windes, it warneth them
of rockes, fhalowes, fandes, & infinite like dangers. In trauailing by
land, her tables poynteth which way to folow, that thy iornay may be
fpedier, fafe, fhort, & plefant, wher you fhall afcend vp to hilles, wher
to paffe ouer waters, where to walke through woodes, and wher moft
aptly to remaine at night. If al thefe were not (as it ferueth to infinite
vfes more then time will permit to repete,) yet this one were fufficiët
tu kepe it in honor , that by it, in fo fmall à lumpe, or piece of clay , be=
holding fuch ftrange formes of men, beaftes, foules, aud fifhes. fuch di=
uerfitie of times, fuch burning hilles, fuch merueilous ftones, metalles
& plants, we are inforced to confeffe th'omnipotency, and wonderous
worke uf God. This is it, that prouoked Diofcorides to leaue cities, &
townes, & trauail into deferts, & wods, to ferch the nature of herbes
This caufed Atlas, Ptolomæus, & Alfonce, to be fo diligët in fetting
out the heauens courfe, & forme of this earthly manfion. The vtilitye
of this , alured Orpheus, Solon, Democritus, Pythagoras, Eudoxus,
Plato, Hipparchus, Polybius, Strabo , & an hundreth more of the
auncient Philofophers, to leaue their country, frends & acquaintāce,
not doubting perel of the feas, dāgers of enemies, loffe of fubftāce, we=
rines of body: or anguifh of mind. Yea the fweatnes therof was fo great
that Strabo after his trauails faid, that if any arte were requifite for
à Philofopher: it was Cofmographie. And Homer called Vliffes the wi
feft among the Græcians, becaufe he knew the natures of people , and
the diuerfitie of nations: Adding, that his eloquence, prudence, forti=
tude, conftancye, & other like vertues (mete for à man) infued of hys
perigrinations, & trauails, which remaining at home, he fhuld neuer
haue learned by any preceptes, difcipline, or teacher. But feing diuers
in oure age are defirous of knowledge no leffe then the Philofophers
were, & yet can not trauaile for the difcorde of nations , the fondrye
fectes of people, and diuers other impedimentes, our refuge is, to faye
with Propertius.

Cogor

THE PRAEFACE.

Cogor et è Tabula, pictos ediscere Mundos.
In Tables set out, Countries to decerne
Constrained am I, and eke for to learne.

In which, I had almoste (through making ouer much haſt) forgot-
ten to reſight the benefits we receiue of Coſmographie: in that ſhe de-
liuereth vs from greate and continuall trauailes. For in à pleaſaunte
houſe, or warme ſtudy, ſhe ſheweth vs the hole face of all th'Earthe,
withal the corners of the ſame. And from this perigrination, thy wife
with ſheadinge ſalte teares, thy children with lamentations, nor thy
frendes with wordes ſhal dehort & perſwade the. In trauailing, thou
ſhalt not be moleſted with the inclemencye of th'Aere, boyſterous
windes, ſtormy ſhoures, haile, Iſe, & ſnow. Comming to thy lodginge,
thou ſhalt not haue à churliſh & vnknowne hoſte, which ſhall myni-
ſter meate twiſe ſodden, ſtinking fiſh, or watered wine. Going to reſt,
thou ſhalt not feare lowſy beddes, or filthy ſheates. In Somer, the ſone
with his fierye beames, ſhall not vexe thee: nor yet in winter, ſtormye
Saturnus ſhal make thy beard froſen. In ſayling, thou ſhalt not dread
Pirates, feare Peries and greate windes, or haue à ſicke ſtomacke
through vnholſome ſmelles. Therfore theſe things conſidered, who is
not incoraged to acheue ſuche an interprice, as ſhall redounde to his
countries fame, & his perpetuall memorye? what wiſe man dothe not
delite to reade ſuch thinges, as Emperoures, Kinges & Princes haue
painfully trauailed in, eſteming ther labours plentuouſlye rewarded,
with the frute of this Art? But leaſt theſe my wordes, ſhould ſtirre vp
the greadye appetides of diuers to this knowledge, & then to wante
herein that mighte ſatiſfie the ſame, beholde I haue compiled this my
Coſmographical glaſſe. By which, ſuch as are delighted in trauailing
as well by land, as water, ſhal receiue no ſmall comfort (If I be not deceiued) & th'other ſort, by it may alſo protract, & ſet out perticuler
cardes for anye countrye, Region, or prouince: or els th'vniuerſall face
of th'earth in à generall Mappe. Firſte if they deſcribe Parallele circles in the Mappe, anſweringe to the like circles in the heauens: & by
the right or croked Horizont, th'equinoctiall, polary circles, and altitude of the pole, to limite out the Zones, Climates, & Paralleles of
Longitude, and Latitude: which being once præpared, you ſhall place
there in the countries, hilles, fluddes, ſeas, fortreſſes, Ilandes, cities,
deſertes, & ſuch like (according to the præcepts of th'art) as are placed on the platte forme of th'earthe. And that the præceptes myghte
ſeme

seme the more facile & plaine, I haue reduced it into the forme of à
Dialoge: the names of the personages in dede fained, but yet most apt=
ly seruing our institutiō. In which Spoudæus (repræsenting the Scho
ler) maketh doubtes, asketh Questions, obiecteth: yea, & some tyme,
digresseth not from the fonde imaginations of the grosse witted. Vn=
to which, Philonicus (suppliyng th' office of à teacher) answereth to
to all th' obiections, & giueth præceptes. VVhat diligēce I haue giuen
in time of the Printing, to the correction herof, and also in diuisinge
sundry newe Tables, Pictures, demonstrations, & præceptes : that
you may easely iudge by readyng the same worke. Also what charges
the Printer hath susteined, that his good will might not be wanting,
that shalbe euident conferryng his beautiful Pictures & letters, with
suche workes, as herto hath bene published. And thus I leaue the with
my Cosmographicall Glasse, requiryng that these my trauayles & labours, be not rewarded with ingratitude, or ill reporte. And if for the
difficultie of the worke, any errour escape: remember I am the firste
that euer in oure tongue haue written of this argument, & therfore
am constrained, to finde out the pathe. whiche if it be not at this time
made plaine, smothe & pleasaunt: if God graūt life, & leisure, I trust
so to treade it againe, that both night and day (walking in the
same) thou shalt not misse of the desired Port. Againe fare
well, & fauoure me, as I wishe thy furderaunce in
knowledge.   At Norwich, the xviij.
of Iuly. 1559.

THE FIRST BOOKE OF THE
Cosmographicall Glasse, conteinyng the necessary Princi=
ples required in this Art: and therfore is an Isagoge, or Intro·
duction vnto the hole worke.

The Interloquutors.∴

Philonicus.   Spoudæus.

Spoudæus.

ATELY CAL-
lyng to my remembraunce
the Race that euery mã in
this his trãsitory life haue
to runne: and that faultes
committed in this course,
for want of time, can scar-
slye with great difficultie, *Men happiest*
labour, and diligence, any
thing be amended: I was of force compelled, to confesse
those most happy, whiche vse this time (being so great a *Time the grea-*
treasure) as repentaunce maye take no place. And on *test treasure.*
the other part, those most miserable mẽ (yea, rather Ima- *Men most in-*
ges, and pictures of men, then very men in dede) whiche *fortunate.*
imploy their busy cure & care, in stealing, Idlenes, vayn
pastimes, long sleapes, dronkennes, lasciuious toying, swering, scraping and gatheryng of Plutos corne together,
as though they had more time, then myght be well spent
in the exaltyng of Vertue, supplãting of Vyce, and profiting their Countrie, Frindes, and Consanguinitie. In
time past, folowing only nature as Ruler and guide, men
did more earnestly, (and as it weare with an insatiate
mynde) seke Vertu for hir selfe, and abhorre Vise, for

B   the

the horrible name therof: the we do in our daies, hauing both Nature, Gods preceptes, and politiquè lawes, as our Capitaines and lodesmen. VVhiche abuse of time,

Engeins

Why men in our age, ar not so learned as thei wer in old tyme.

is the greatest cause, that men in our age, are not comparable in any thyng to those of times past. For how many sondry Artes, secrete Sciences, and wonderfull Ingens, throwgh well spending of tyme, did the auncient Philosophers in their dayes inuente? Archimedes deuisyd

The frute springing of well spent tyme.

glasses, with whiche the Siracusians might burne their enemies farre distant, on the seas from them. Ptolomæus, Atlas, and Alphonsus (being kinges) founde out the maruelous course and sondry motions, of the supercelestiall bodies: writyng sondry volumes of them, to the great comfort of such, as ar lyuing at this presente. Appollo, first founde Physicke the repayrer of health. And in lyke maner, some one thing, and some an other, of whose Godly trauelles so many precious monumentes yet remayne: yea and the Authors them selues (being dead so many hundred yeares sence) are as freshe in the minde of mã, as it were but yesterday, such is the reward of vertuouse trauell. But whome do I se walking in yonder grene place, among the pleasaunt byrdes, flowers, and trees, is it not Philonicus? It is he: I will go and salute him. God the giuer of all sapience and science, saue you (ryght reuerent Philonicus.) I accompte my selfe happy, that I haue founde you: for now my hope is, to be deliuered (although not of all yet) of some of the bondes, and chaynes, of Ignoraunce.

Philonicus.   You are vnfaynedly welcome to me at this

this prefent: and lyke as your name is *Spoudæus*: fo you do in no point degenerate frõ the fame: but are diligẽt in feking knowledge, efchewing idlenes, and vain paftimes.

Spoudæus.   That J learned, taking at you example: for you euer keping perpetual warre with ignorãce, and vife of euery kinde: (for rewarde wherof vertu alfo gaue you that name) do vfe to reade, and reuolue the trefure of Sapiẽce, J meane, the fecrete workes of Nature fhut vp, or rather conteyned, in the worthy and auncient writers. And in reading certaine of them, J haue found not only matters of great difficultie: but alfo (as to me it femeth) of muche vntruthe.

Philonicus.   You muft iudge well of their laboures whiche haue before our dayes written: for time bryngeth thinges to their perfection. Jf we without any grounde, fhould by our vigilancie, fynde out fuche mifteries, yea and (as J may terme them) hid fecretes of Nature: J affure you, we fhould haue left many more errours to our pofteritie, then they haue in their writynges vnto vs. Yea and there are many thinges whiche feme falfe and vntrue: bycaufe the groffe capacities, of vnlearned perfons, can not redely comprehende the fame. But wherof doe thofe Authours intreate, in whiche you haue fo latelye traueled?

Spoudæus.   They be wryters of Cofmographie, Geographie, Hydrographie, or Nauigation. But becaufe that ether they obferue no order, or Methode in their teaching, ether that they digreffe from that they take in hande (and fyll their volumes with other fciẽces,

rather then Cosmographie.) J haue very lyttle profyted
by my trauell.

Philo.   J reioyce that your fortune was to take in
hande suche authors. For Cosmographie in my iudgement is mete for euery estate, and moste excellent of all
other naturall science. Wherfore be you nothing discom-
fortid, and amasyd with the difficultie of their wryting.
For howe muche the thinge transcende in worthynes o-
ther knowledge not so plausible : so muche the more it is
companion with dificultie. And where as you alleadge,
that the most part of them obserue no Methode, and order: in that J will doe my indeuour, (as also in the other,
where place shall require) to suplie that wante in that
behalfe.

Spoud.   You shall meruailouslye incourage me, and
take away the greatest trouble in this my study, if you do
not only showe me the knowledge therof in suche order,
as J may best conceiue it: but also explicate, and opē such
placis, as are obscure and darke for me to vnderstande.

Philo.   Yet before we take in hande this studie, there
is one thing, of whiche J must haue knowledge (that is)

Arithmetick and Geometry necessary for this art. whether you haue redde any authours of Arithmetick,
and Geometry: els you had best reade some of them, and
resorte to me againe at some other conuenient season.

Spoud.   Yes sir J haue redde the ground of Artes,
The whestone of wytte, and the path way.

Philonicus.   That J am glad to vnderstande: so shal
it be the easier for me to instructe you, and you better to
conceyue, and also retayne the surer, suche thinges as
shalbe

ſhalbe taught. For he that wyll couer the roufe of his houſe, before he haue made the foundation, and buildyd the walles: beſyde the loſſe of his coſt, ſhall be thought ſcarſe a wytty builder. But J wil exhort you as time ſhal ſeme mete alſo to reade with great diligence Orontius Arithmeticke, Scheubelius Algeber, Euclides Elemē- taries, and Theodoſius of ſpherike Demonſtrations: not only for this ſtudies ſake whiche you now haue in hande: but for all other artes (whiche taſte of the Mathematicalles) that you ſhall here after trauell in. But nowe to the ſcope that you deſire. And becauſe that you maye knowe, wherof the matter depende of whiche we ſhall intreate, let me here what you call Coſmographie.

Orontius.
Scheubelius.
Euclide.
Theodoſius.

Spoud. That ſemeth vnto me to be none other thing, then the arte whiche doe ſet forth, and deſcribe the vniuerſall worlde.

What Coſmographie is.

Philo. You haue ſayd rightly, for ſo the Etymologie of this word Coſmographie doth ſound. But is there no diference betwixt this worde Coſmographie, and Geographie?   Spoud. Jt ſhould ſo ſeme to me, for both do deſcribe the worlde.

Philo. Then define you Geographie, after ſuche authours myndes as you haue redde.

Spoud. That wyll J doe gladly. Ptolomæus in his geographie defineth it in this ſorte.

Lib. 1. cap. 1.

Η γεωγραφία, μίμησίς ἐςι διαγραφῆς τȣ κατειλημμένȣ τῆς γῆς μέρȣς ὅλȣ, μετὰ τῶν ὡς ἐπίπαν αὐτȣ συνημμένων.

What Geographie is.

  Whiche ſentence J turning into Latyne ſoundith
  in this ſorte.

Geographia eſt vniuerſarum terræ partium cognitarū, vnà cum hiis, quæ ei veluti vniuerſaliter coniunᴄta ſunt, piᴄturæ imitatio.

whiche

Whiche in our tongue is as muche to saye as.

Geographie is the imitation, and discriptiõ of the face, and picture of th'earth, with her partes knowen, and of such things as are to it cõnected and ioyned.

Philo. You haue truly repetyd Ptolomæus worde.

Now J wyll proue by your disinition, that you haue erred two wayes, in putting no diference betwixt Cosmographie, and Geographie. First Cosmographie teacheth the discriptiõ of the vniuersal world, and not of th'earth only: and Geographie of th'earth, and of none other part.

Spoud. Why syr, make you a diference betwixt the worlde, and th'earth?

Philo. Yea verely, and that as much as betwixt a mã, and his litle finger, but of that, you shal heare more or we departe. The seconde way you erryd in the order of diuiding th'earth: for albeit Cosmographie describeth the face of th'earth, yet it is by noting and obseruing certaine diuisions, answering vnto .v. principal paralleles or equidistant circles in the heauens. As they dwell in the middes of th'earth that inhabit vnder th'equinoctiall lyne, and the like of the dwellers vnder th'other circles, is said On th'other parte, Geographie doe deliniat, and set out the vniuersal earth, no respect had vnto the fornãed circles of the heauẽs: but by Hylles, Moũtayns, Seas, fluddes, and such other nutable thinges, as are in it cõteined.

Spoud. Then by your wordes J also gather, there is some diference betwyxt these two, and Chorographie.

Philo. Yea and that Ptolomæus in the place of you alleadgid, do playnly expresse. For lyke as Cosmographie describeth the worlde, Geographie th'earth: in lyke sorte

Corogra-

The diference of Cosmographie and Geographie.

What Chorographie is and howe it difereth from the other two.

Chorographie, sheweth the partes of th'earth, diuided in
them selues. And seuerally describeth, the portes, Riuers
Hauens, Fluddes, Hilles, Moūtaynes, Cities, Villages,
Buildinges, Fortresses, Walles, yea and euery particuler thing, in that parte conteined. And is in respect saith
he, of Cosmographie and Geographie, as if a paiter shuld
set forth the eye, or eare of a man, and not the whole body, so that Chorographie consisteth rather in describyng
the qualitie and figure, then the bignes, and quantitie of
any thinge.

Spoud.   Although by your wordes, J haue receiued
more commoditie at this present, then by all my readyng
touching the true diference of these three names: yet if it
may please you to geue me the figures of euery of them, I
shall so stedfastly printe it in my mynde, as I truste not to
forget them, for it is truly said, thinges sene haue longer
impresion then only harde.

Thinges seene
are lenger in
mynde, then
only harde.

Philo.   J wyll gladly fulfill your requeste. Marke nowe
this example folowing. Here first you do see the heauens
conteine in them th'earth.

¶ This figure reprasent the forme
of Cosmographie.

Whiche earth is deuided
into fiue principall partes,
accordinge to the fiue Circles in the heauens : the
names of whiche for bre-
uitie J omytte vntyll conuenient place, lest thorowe
oftē repeting things thei at
length seme tedious . The
other

other fygure without circles, reprefenteth th'earth, fet
forth with Waters, Hylles, Mountaynes, and fuch like.

This Picture
aunfwereth vn=
to Geographie.

And finally for Chorographie, I haue placed th'excellēt
Citie of Norwyche, as the forme of it is, at this prefent
1558. Nowe that you haue learned their difference,
declare in which of thē you moft delight to be inftructed.
Spoud. J thanke you fyr, I fhall neuer be able (more
then with praier) to recompence your paynes. But fence

Cofmographie
excelleth Geo-
graphie and
Chorographie.

Cofmographie is more excellent then the other two, both
for the manifolde vfe, and that it cōteineth and compre-
hendeth the other in it felfe : I would imploye my whole
induftrie herein.

Philo. Then feing that Cofmographie defcribeth the
worlde as you haue fayde, (and that rightly) it is neceffary to know what the world is, what the partes of it are,

The argumēt
of the whole
worke.

and how many, yea and finally, by what meanes, as well
the world, as alfo the partes of it, ar defcribed. This perfitly lernyd, haue you then for this prefent, your whole
defire? Spoud. Yes verely.

Philo.

THE DECLARATION OF THE PRINCIPAL
places in the Citie, after th' order of th' Alphabete.

A   Thorpe VVoode.
B   S. Leonardes.
C.   The place where men are cuſtomablie burnt.
D.   Biſhoppes Gate.
E.   The Cathedrall church, called Chriſtes Churche.
F.   S. Martins at the Pallis Gate.
G   Pokethorpe Gates.
H.   The Suburbs called Pokthorpe.
I.   .Magdalene gates
K   S. Butholdes.
M   S. Clementes.
N   S. Auguſtines.
P.   S, Auguſtines Gates.
Q.   S. Martines Gates.
R.   S Martines at th' Ooke.
S.   The new milles.
T.   Hell gates, the Suburbs ioyning to it, called Heiham.
V   S. Benets Gates.
VV S. Giles Gates.

X.   S. Stephens Gates.
Y.   Braſen dore.
Z.   S. Iohns gates.
&.   Lakenam VVoode.
AA Chuppell in the fielde.
BB Eaten VVoode.
CC The Caſtell.
DD The hoſpitall.
EE The market place.
FF S. Peters permantigate.
GG S. Martines on the hill.
HH. S. Iohns on the hill.
II   S. Michaels.
LL S. Iohns at the gates.
MM S. Stephens.
NN Thorpe.
QQ In the righthand is that part of the riuer Yerus coming from Yermouth, and renneth thorow the City.
QQ The left hand th' other part of the forſaid riuer going hier into the countrye.

This Picture muſt be placed before the 9. leafe.

Philonicus. Then let vs beginne with the defi-nition of the worlde, whiche the auncient Cleomedes de-finith in this maner.

Lib. primo in initio.

Κόσμος ἐστὶ σύστημα ἐξ οὐρανοῦ καὶ γῆς, καὶ τῶν ἐν τούτῳ φύσεων. οὗτος δὲ πάντα μὲν τὰ σώματα ἐμπεριέχει, οὐδενὸς ἁπλῶς ἐκ τοσαύτου ὑπέρχοντος.

And J do tranſlate it into Latine as foloweth.

What the Worlde is.

Mundus eſt ex cælo, terraq; , ac naturis deniq; in eis compræhenſis, compages. Is autem corpora in ſe ſingula continet , nec extra eum, prorſus quicquam cernitur.

That is, the world is an apte frame, made of heauen, and earth, & of thinges in them conteyned. This comprehēdeth all thinges in it ſelf, nether is there any thing without the lymites of it viſible.

Whiche definition differith not from Ariſtotle and o-ther famous writers. So that what ſo euer is betwixt the ſeate of the almighty gouernour of all lyuing creatures, and the center of the earth : is called the worlde. And is compared to à round ball and globe.

Ariſtotle.

Spoudæus. Then all that we ether by ſyght may decerne , or by arte conceiue , that ſame is the worlde. And conteyneth in it what ſo euer the eternall Creater, by his wounderfull worke haue in this circuit bleſſed, and made. **Philonicus.** True it is.

Spoud. Then J perceiue my error before cōmitted, wheare J applied this worde worlde, only to the earth.

The Worlde and the earth not one thing.

Philonicus. So in lyke ſorte it is otherwayes abu-ſed, but note you diligently that is ſaide before of Cleo-medes and it ſhalbe ſufficient.

Spoudæus. And is there nothinge beyonde this worlde? my imagination, leadeth me to the contrary.

Philonicus. Jn dede Pythagoras folowing ima-gination , more then Reaſon affirmeth ſumwhat to bee, whiche is not comprehendid with in the worlde: and na-

Pythagoras error.

meth

Plato.
Aristotle.

meth it *Vacuum*. But *Plato*, and *Aristotle*, doe ouer‐
throwe this assertion. And seing that it transsendith the
knowledge of mā let it passe, & retorne we to our matter.
Spoudæus.   What be the partes of the worlde?
Philonicus.   The worlde is made of two partes,

The Worlde made of two partes.

that is to saye, of the Elementary Region, conteinyng in
it the foure Elementes, Fyre, Ayre, Water, and Earth:
and what so euer of them is compounded and made, of
whiche hereafter we shall intreate: and of the heauenlye
region, of which at this present time we wil make mētion.

This Type do represent the world, deuidid in to his two peculiar parts.

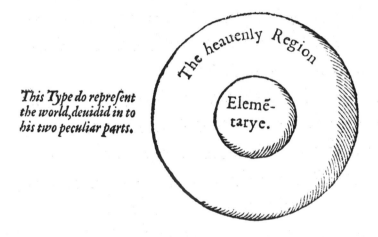

The number of the heauens.

This region do in it contayne .x. spheres, in suche sorte
as the greater comprehendith in him the lesser, as the .x.
heauen or Primum mobile, comprehendith the .ix. hea‐
uen callid also Cristalline. This heauen compasseth the
viij. heauen, called in greke ἀπλανὶς because the sterres
kepe one vniforme distance in mouing, and for that cause
are namid fixid. And so this receiue in this compasse the
sphere of Saturne, Jupiter, Mars, the Sonne, Venus,
Mercu‐

Mercurius, the Mone, and the foure Elementes.

Spoud. *Why should not the spheres of the Sonne, and* An obiection
Mone be aboue the other Planetes, as wel as in that or-
der, you haue rehersed them?

Philo. *This serueth not for our purpose, but it is ex-*
cellently proued of Ptolomæus, Alphraganus, Tebi-
tius, Archimedes, and other, with suche inuinsible rea-
sons as can not be denied. But me thinke the pleasaunt
Poet Ouidius, maketh a good reason to proue the Sonne Ptolomæus.
to haue his sphere, in lyke order as is aforesayde, whan Alphraganus
as he speaketh vnder the parson of Phebus, vnto yonge Tebitius.
Phaëton (entring into his Chariot) in this maner. Archimedes.

Altius egreſſus, cæleſtia ſigna cremabis: Lib.2. Meta-
Inferius terras: medio tutiſſimus ibis. morphoſ.

In our english tunge, the meaning of these versis is thus.
Directe thy Chariot in a meane, clymbe thou not to hye:
Leſt thou doſt burne the heauēly Signes, ſet in the ſterry ſkye.
Or deſcending to lowe th'earth, of heat ſhall fele the flame.
But kepe the meane, ÿ ſhalt be fre, frō feare, & eke frō blame

Spoud. *The cause is so manifest, that it nede no len-*
ger declaration. So that I suppose theis excellēt wryters
aforesaid, haue found out the true order of the spheres as
you haue repeted them. And that Crates with his com- The error of
pany, haue no lesse erred, placing the luminaries aboue Crates
the eyght heauen: then Albetragnius whiche supposeth Albetragnius
Venus: and Democritus, whiche affirmeth Mercurye, Democritus
to be higher then the Sonne. and Plato.

Philo. *Yea and Plato, (whiche otherwyse is a graue*
Philosopher) did no lesse erre then the other, imagi-
ning the luminaries to haue their course vnder all the
other Planetes.

Spoud.

Spoud. *Well let them paſſe, and now to the nomber of the heauens, whiche you affirme to be.x.*

Philoni. *You haue ryghtly ſpoken.*

Spoud. *I remember among other thinges that I haue redde in Diodorus, howe that the Ægiptians ſuppoſed there were but eyght heauens : and that by this perſwaſion. They gaue to the ſeuen Planetes.vij.heauens. And bycauſe they perceiued that heauen (whiche you call the firmamēt) to cary the fixed ſterres in it, and to kepe one vniforme order and diſtaunce in ryſing, none ſteed, and going downe: to circuit th'earth alſo in. 24. houres: and finally, to cary the heauens of the Planetes, by his ſwiftnes about th'earth with him, contrary to their naturall motion, they ſuppoſed (of whoſe mynde I alſo am) that there ware but eight heauens. And that, which you call the eight heauen, they name primum mobile.*

Philo. *You may not to raſhely adicte your ſelfe to any of their opinions, before you are certaine they are eyther trew, or els receiued as moſte probable . For by the lyke reaſon, I can compell you to confeſſe there are. ix. heauens, as Ptolomæus affirmeth. But for ſhortnes of time, and that it ſumwhat ſwaruith from our purpoſe, I wyll omytte it: and leane to th'authoritie of the famous king, and graue Philoſopher Alphonſus : whoſe name by his trauell, is made immortall.*

Spoud. *Thus I perceiue your ſaiynge to be verified (when you excuſed the olde writers) that tyme, bryng all thinges to their perfection . But I haue redde alſo of an heauen, whiche in greke is named Ἐμπύριον, Empyreū.*

Philo.

The Ægiptiãs found out but 8. heauens.

Ptolomæus found out the 9. heauen.

Alfonſus firſt founde the. 10 heauen out.

Philo. It is so named of the wonderful brightnes, and
beautie. But becauſe it is imoble, and without any mouїg
I exclude it out from the nūber of the mouable heaũẽs:
and that, as not ſeruing to our purpoſe . And thus you
haue learned what the worlde is , and alſo the heauenly
region. But for the redier conceiuing of that whiche is
now ſpoken, behold the figure inſuing.
Spou. Wil it pleaſe you now to procede with th'elemẽ-
tarye region,
which you de-
clared to be
th'other parte
of the world?
Philo. Be-
fore we ſhall
take this part
in hande (for
the eaſier a-
uoyding often
repetitiõ of one
thing) I wyll
giue you ſome

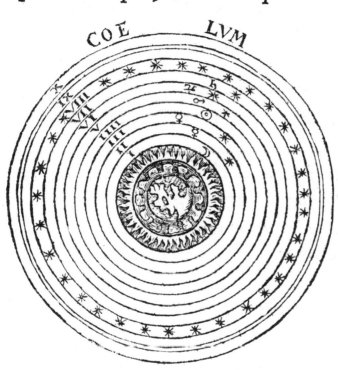

COELVM

introduction into the celeſtiall ſphere, touching ſuch circles as muſt of neceſſitie ſerue in this arte.
Spou. And that fault haue troubled, yea right excellent authors, for they obſeruїg no methode, were cõpelled
to repete one thing diuers, and ſondry times. But becauſe you made mention of a ſphere, maye it pleaſe you to
make definition of it?

                    C.   Philo.

Philo. *All suche as haue wryten hereof, do accorde in one as Theodosius, Proclus, Euclyde, Orontius, Iohn Halifax our worthy countryman, (called also Iohn de sacrobosco.) &c. But as well for th'authoritie, as also elegancie, I wyll repete vnto you Theodosius definition, who sayth in this wyse.*

Theodosius.
Proclus.
Euclide.
Orontius.
Iohn Halifax

Lib.1. prop. 1. Σφαῖρα, ὅτι σχῆμα στετεὸν ὑπὸ μιᾶς ἐπιφανείας περιεχόμενον, πρὸς ἕω ἀφ᾽ ἑνὸς σημείου τῶν ἐντὸς τῶ σχήματος κειμένων, πᾶσαι ὰι προσπίπτουσαι εὐθεῖαι, ἴσαι ἀλλήλαισ εἰσίν.

Sphæra est figura solida cōprehēsa v nā superficie, ad quā ab vno eoru pūctorū quæ ītra figurā sūt, oēs rectæ lineæ ductæ sūt inter se æquales

A sphere is a sound body, conteined within one platte forme and bounde, vnto whiche all right lynes drawen from the Center, (they being cōteyned within the figure) are founde æqual amōg thē selues. To the vnderstanding of whiche definitiō, is requisite to knowe both what the center, axe tree, and diameter of a sphere is.

Spoud. *Now I perceiue the reading of the pathway doth not a lytle helpe me, in vnderstanding this definitiō of Theodosius: as also suche wordes, whiche are vsuall in Geometry. But what is this axe tree of the sphere? for I vnderstand that by a center is nothing mete, but a prick in the myddes of any circumference.*

What a cēter is.

Philo. *Theodosius, calleth the axe tree, a certain right line drawen by the center, both endes of it ending in the plat forme of the said sphere, the sphere being turned about it: and yet this axe tree to remaine fixid & without motion. As in exāple. Here you se A.B.C. to represent the halfe sphere, the axe tree also drawen through it is A. D.C. whiche being fixid, & the halfe spheare turnynge round*

Lib.1. prop.3.

What the axe tree is.

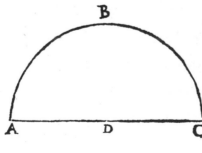

round about, maketh a parfait rouͤd body. As this figure
here placed maketh true mention.

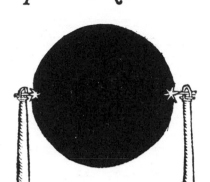

Spoud. J pray you what
difference is there betwixt
the diameter of a ſpheare
and the axe tree.

Philo. J wil ſhowe you,
omitting th'auctors names
for briefnes. A diameter
of a ſphere, or globe, is any
lyne drawen thorowe the
same, goyng by the center of the ſphere, or globe. And ſo
there may be (yea and you wyll). xx. diameters, or as
many as you pleaſe in a ſphere : but there can be but one
axe tree, on whiche the ſphere, or globe, is reuoluid. And
this axe tree is voyde of all motion.

Spoud. J wil (and it pleaſe you) make a profe wherby
you ſhal perceiue, if J rightly vnderſtad your meaning.

Philo. do you ſo. Spou. Here J wyl make a ſphere,

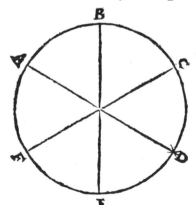

in whiche I drawe right lines,
frō the one part of the circūfe-
rēce, by the cēter, & ſo to th'o-
ther. Such right lines, or diameters, are AD : CF : BE :
but I do imagine only A.D. to
be the axe tree, and imoble.

Philo. Very wel wrought.
Now procede we forth. You muſt alſo conſider that the
ſphere is deuided, into a right ſphere and into an oblique
or crokyd ſphere.

What a dia-
meter is, and
how it dife-
reth from the
axe tree afor-
ſayd.

C.ij.　　　　　they

The ſpheare is
taken two
wayes.
A right ſphere
The poles of
the worlde
what thei are.
they only haue a right ſphere which dwell vnder th'equinoctiall, and haue both the pole arctike, and antarctick
in their Horizont.

Spoud.　Do you not call the two pointes or endes of the
axe tree, the fornamed poles?

Philo.　It is ſo, and for firmer printing it in memory,
beholde here the type of them that haue a right ſphere.

As A. D. C. repreſenteth
bothe the axe tree, and the
right Horizont: and A. C. the
two poles: Yea and B. D. the
half parte of th'equinoctiall.
Spoud.　So that a mã inha-
biting vnder B. D. which is th'equinoctial, do perceiue
both A. whiche is the North pole, and C. whiche is the
South, leuell with th'earth, and his verticall point, in the
forſaid Æquinoctial.　Philo.　You do well perceyue it.
Spoud.　Then it foloweth, that where ether of the poles, is eleuated aboue th'earth, they dwell not vnder the
An oblique
or croked
ſphere.
æquinoctial, and ſo haue a croked, & an oblique ſphere.

Philo.　And that doe this
figure perfitly proue. Here
C. E. is the halfe of the axe
tree aboue th'earth, B. E. is
the halfe of th'equinoctial. C.
the one pole aboue th'earth. Whiche maketh the halfe
ſphere. A. B. C. D. to be oblique, and croked, according to my firſt meanig. Spou.　I vnderſtãd this perfitly
Philo.　Then is it expediẽt for you to cõſider, that this
ſphere

sphere doeth in it conteine many Circles.

Spoud. *Your wordes bringe me in à doubt. For I perceiue that à circle, & à sphere are both rounde, & haue
like Centers, & Diameters.*

Phil. *They haue no lesse, yet they do as greatlye differ
as the worlde, & th'earth (of which we made mention)
as this definition of Euclid, do manifest plainly.*

Κύκλος, ἐστὶ σχῆμα ἐπίπεδον, ὑπὸ μιᾶς γραμμῆς περιεχόμενον, ἣ καλεῖται Περιφέρεια, πρὸς Lib.1.defi.14.
ἓν ἀφ' ἑνὸς σημείου τῶν ἐντὸς τῦ σχήματος κειμένων, πᾶσαι ἀι προσπίπτουσαι εὐθεῖαι ἴσαι
ἀλλήλαις ἐισί.

which Scheubel.excellētly (after his maner) trāslateth.

Circulus est figura plana, vna linea compræhensa, quæ circumfe-
rḗntia appellatur, ad quam ab vno quodam puncto eorum, quæ intra
figuram sunt posita, omnes cadḗtes rectæ lineæ inter se sunt æquales.

And is thus much to say with vs.

*A Circle is à plaine and flat figure comprehended within one line,
which is called à circumference: vnto whiche, if lines be drawne from
the Center, or poynt of the circle, vnto the circumference, they beinge
conteined within the same, are found to be equall one to an other.*

*As in this example. A.
is the center of the Circle:
B.C.D.E. the Circum-
ferent line.&c.*

Spou. *By these wordes
J finde à twofoulde diffe-* How a sphere
and a Circle
differ.
*rence betwixt à sphere, &
à circle. First, that à circle
is à playne, & flat figure,
& à sphere of rŏude fourme, like vnto à Ball. And then
that à Circle is cōpræhended within one line, & a sphere
within one plat fourme. But now J pray you declare such
Circles, as are imagined to be in the sphere of the worlde,
& most necessary for an introduction.*

C iij. Philo.

Phil. *In This sphere chiefly x. Circles are imagined: Of whiche 6.be great, & 4. be small: whiche in order I will set out. And therfore answer me: Haue you not read among your authours of the Horizōt circle ? we will beginne with that firste, because necessitie inforseth suche order.*

Spou. *Yes sir: Proclus defineth it in this sorte.*

Ὁρίζων δὲ ἐστὶ κύκλος ὁ διορίζων ἡμῖν τό τε φανερὸν καὶ τὸ ἀφανὲς μέρος τȣ κόσμου· καὶ διχοτομῶν τὴν ὅλην σφαῖραν τȣ κόσμȣ, ὥστι ἡμισφαίριον μὲν ὑπὲρ γῆν ἀπολαμβάνεσθαι, ἡμισφάιριον δὲ ὑπὸ γῆν.

Horizon est circulus qui diuidit nobis mundi partem, quæ videtur, ab ea quæ non apparet: & qui ita in duas partes æquales totum discindit mundi globum, vt eius dimidia pars altera supra terrā extet, dimidia altera sub terra sit.

Which sounded in our language in this maner.

The Horizont is à Circle which deuideth, & parteth that part of the world which we see, from that which do not appere: & which parteth the worlde in two equall partes, in suche facion, as th'one halfe is euer aboue th'earth, th'other alway vnder.

Phil. *Th'use of this Circle is right excellent, for by it we finde out the rysing, & goyng downe of euery Planet & Starre. In this Horizont the daye & nyghte, haue also theyr beginning, & ende.*

Spou. *So that this Horizont is à lyne imagined to go rounde about by the face of th'earth, parting the heauens in two partes, and is saide of ὁρίζω, whiche signifieth to decerne, or ende. But standing on an hie Mountaine,*

steple, or suche lyke thing, shal I se but halfe the heauēs,

Philo. *Yes verely, you shall see more then an Hemis-*

phere (for so call they the halfe sphere) as also beynge in à valley and lowe place, you shall not see youre Hemisphere totally. And althoughe you may obiecte, that this Horizont deuideth not the heauen in two equal portiōs,

　　　　　　　　　　　　　　　　　　yet it

yet it is proueth nothinge : for th'Aſtrologians alowe no
ſuche Horizont.

Spoud.   And is this Horizont à fixed Circle or not?

Philo.   Jt is fixed, and without motion.

Spou: Jt ſhould ſeme contrary. For I beynge at Lon- *An obiection*
don haue one Horizont, and goyng to Andwerpe, haue
an other, and ſo at Colein an other, and at Heydelberge
another.&c.

Philo.   J confeſſe no leſſe, but that proueth nothinge *Th'aunſwere.*
that the horizont moueth, for loke into what errour you
ſhoulde fall : you muſte graunte (if the horizont moue)
that with the turning of the heauens, your horizont Circle muſt come ouer your verticall poĩt, once in 24. houres.

Spoud.   Nay, I will not graunt ſuche abſurditie in
any caſe: wherfore I ſee that it is my chaũgyng that maketh me to haue à newe horizont, and not the horizont
to moue with me.

Phil.   You hit the naile on the head (as the ſaying is) *The Horizont*
Nowe your authour deuideth the horizont, lyke to the *deuided into*
ſphere: that is, into à ryght horizont, and into à croked *two partes.*
or oblique.

Spoud.   What be they that haue a right horizont?
Phil.   They haue a right horizont, whan as this *A right Ho-*
circle croſſeth th'equinoctiall.rightely in two partes, and *rizont.*
they haue a croked horizont, whan eyther of the Poles *A croked Ho*
is aboue th'Earth, and th'other vnder : ſuche is oure Ho- *rizont.*
rizont whiche inhabit Europe.   But for the better vnderſtanding, J haue made here a figure, in whiche C. A.
and E. is th'equinoctiall. And becauſe B. A. D .croſ-
ſeth it

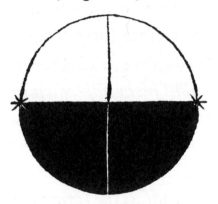

This Picture sheweth the fourme
of a right Horizont.

sith it rightely : It is the
right Horizont. Also B.
D. are the two Poles of
the worlde: & because B.
is eleuated aboue th'earth,
it maketh F. A. G. to be
th'obliquè Horizont , as
these ij. pictures here pla-
ced do shewe.

This Figure represent a croked
or oblique Horizont.

Spoud.   *Seyng that the Horizont semeth onely neces-*
sary for to know the true risinge, & goynge downe of the
Sonne, Mone, Planetes, & fixed sterres, it can not any
thynge helpe for to knowe whan anye of them are at the
hiest aboue the Horizont for that daye, in whiche place
whan as the Sonne cōmeth: it is midday. For I perceiue
euery Planet, & Starre, to ascende by litle, & litle a-
boue th'earth, vntyll they be at the hiest : & then in lyke
maner do continuallye descende , vntill they come to the
Horizont in the West.
Phil.   *For this & diuers other occasions (in times*
past)

paſt)they imagined a circle whiche they called the me-
ridian circle and Proclus, in this ſorte ſetteth it out.

Μεσημ**ε**ρινὸς δ**ὲ** ὅρι κύκλος, ὁ δι**ὰ** τ**ῶν** τ**ᴕ** κόσμ**ᴕ** πόλ**ων** κ**αὶ** τ**ᴕ** κατὰ κορυφὴν σημεί**ᴕ** ρρα=
φό**μ**ἐνος . ἐφ̕ ὁυ γενό**μ**ἐνος ὁ ἥλιος τα μέσα τ**ῶν** ἡμερ**ῶν**, κ**αὶ** τὰ μέσα τ**ῶν** νυκτ**ῶν** ποιεῖται.
Meridianus circulus is eſt, qui deſcribitur per polos mūdi, & per ver-
ticis punctum, in quo cum fuerit ſol, facit diei noctiſq; dimidium.

The meridiane or middaie circle (ſaith he) is deſcribid and dra=
wen by the poles of the worlde, and the point directlye ouer oure
heades called Zenit* in whiche whan the Sonne entreth (whiche is
twyſe in a naturall day)it is mydday, or mydnight.

Spoud. *Yea and this meridiane by Theodoſius pro-*
bation, ſhall in all places croſſe rightly the Horizont, &
is alſo a fixid circle as the Horizont is.

Philo. *And that was one of the greateſt reaſons (if*
I be not deceiued) whiche prouoked the Aſtronomers to
make their computation from midday. And as many as
dwell either plaine North, or South, haue the ſame me-
ridiane that you haue : and ſuche as are either Eaſt, or
Weſt, haue an other meridian, and not the ſame whiche
you haue.

Spoud. *Then by your wordes I gather that the inha-*
bitantes whiche be directly vnder vs (the Geographers
name them Antipodes)are vnder the ſame meridiane
lyne, that we be.

Philo. *Verely it is true.*
But we wyll omyt the de-
claration of them vntyll
our next metinge, and I
wyll gyue you example of
the meridiane circle, ioy-
ned with the Horizont.
Here you ſe A. E. C. re-
preſent

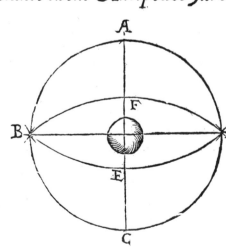

What the Me-
ridian is.

* Zenit is that
point or prick
imagined to be
directly ouer
our heades &
is alwaye.90.
degrees frō the
Eaſt, South,
Weaſt, and
North.
Lib. 1.prop.3.

Antipodes.

preſent the verticall point, B. D. the poles of the world, by whiche and A. (being the vertical circle) is the meridiã circle A. B. C. D. delineated and drawẽ. Whiche croſſeth alſo B. E. D. F. being the Horizont circle.

Spoud.　This circle I do wel remembre, but I do furder perceiue that the Sõne riſeth not alway at one time, and therfore is ſometime longer or he come to the meridian, and ſometime ſhorter, ſo that the daies increaſe and decreaſe continually, except twyſe euery yeare. (Which is to ſaye the. x. of Marche, and the. xiiij. of Septẽber) and then the daies, and nightes are equall, and he ryſeth directly Eaſt, and ſetteth playne Weſt: whiche in other times, he do not, as we may dayly vnderſtande.

Philo.　The diference of the tymes, ingendred by the courſe of the Sonne, you ſhall eaſely fynde by th'quinoctiall.

Spoud.　you renew that, whiche almoſte was out of my memory. For I reading the forſayd Proclus, remẽber he maketh mention of th'equinoctiall circle in this wyſe.

Ἰσημερινὸς δὲ κύκλος ἐςὶν ὁ μέγιστος τῶν πέντε παραλλήλων κύκλην, ὁ διχοτομούμϑϟος ὑπὸ τȣ ὁρίζωντος, ὥστε ἡμικύκλιον ὑπὲρ γῆν ἀπολαμϐάνεσθαι, ὑμικύκλιον δὲ ὑπὸ τὸν ἐριζωντα, ἐφ' ȣ γενόμϑϟος ὁ ἥλιος τὰς ἰσημερίας ποιεῖται τὴν ἐαρινὴν καὶ τὴν φθινοπωρινὴν.

Aequinoctialis autem circulus eſt horum quinque parallelorũ maximus, ita ab horizonte in duoſectus, vt eius dimidia pars altera ſit ſupra terram, altera vero ſub terra: in quo cum fuerit ſol, æquinoctia facit duo, vernũ & Autumnale.

Th'equinoctiall is a circle greateſt of all th'other. v. Paralleles, and is ſo deuided, and parted of the Horizont, that th'one halfe is euer aboue th'earth, and th'other halfe vnder: into whiche, whan the Sonne enter (whiche is twyſe yearly ſpring tyme, and harueſt) the daies and nightes are equall thorowe the whole earth.

Philo.

Philo. *Moreouer you must further consider that this circle difereth from the other two afore said because it is mouable, and caried about with the heauens, where the other are stedfast and fixid.*

Spoud. *It must nedes so be. But are not the poles of this circle, the poles of the worlde?*

Philo. *Yes verely, and they that dwell vnder th'equinoctiall haue the signes equally ascending, and descending, whiche should not be, if the poles of it, did varie frō the poles of the worlde. That they do ascende, and also descend equally, Lucan th'excellent Poet, do aptly set out, where he describeth Cato his voyage into Lybia, which is towarde th'equinoctial, in these versis annexid.* *Lib.9.*

Non obliquè meant, nec Tauro rectior exit
   Scorpius, aut Aries donat sua tempora Libræ.
Aut Astrea iubet lentos descendere Pisces.
   Par Geminis, Chiron: & idem quòd Carcenus ardens
Humidus Aegoceros, nec plus Leo tollitur Vrna.

The meaning of whiche versis in English meater is,
The signes in equall tymes, do ascend and descende:
   The Ballance and the Ramme, the Scorpion and Bull.
The Twinnes and Archer eke, the Crabe and Goate defende:
   The fearse Lyon, the Pot with water that is full.
The Virgin with her braunche, soner cannot apere:
   Then the Fysshes by course approche to the west nere.

Spoud. *I shall and it please you make a proue hereof as I did in the other, wher by you may correcte my error, if any shall folowe: and then you may procede with the other circles.* *Philoni.* *Doe you so.*

Spoud. *I haue here made a figure in whiche C. E. do represent th'equinoctiall. B. A. D. the axe tree of the worlde. B. the north pole or arcticke, and D. in lyke sort th'antracticke,* th'antarcticke, whiche are also the poles of th'equinoc tiall.

Philo. I do muche commende you. Nowe further more you maye consyder, that lyke as the rising, and going downe of the Sonne, Moone, and Planetes, is founde out by the helpe of the Horizont: their true height by the meridian circle: and the varietie of tyme by th'equinoctiall:(comparing the quantitie of the daye present, vnto the quantitie of the day whan as the Sõne is in th'equinoctial)so there is also a proper path, or way, in whiche the other Planetes, as well as the Sonne do finyshe their reuolutiõ, and course, according to their true tyme . Whiche circle is very nedefull for Geographers, as hereafter you shall vnderstande.

Spoud. I pray you sir, is not that the circle, whiche I haue in a starry nyght decernid lyke a brode gyrdle full of starres, in whiche also in some part is the mylkey way called as I suppose γαλαξίας of Ptolomæus, and of Tully lacteus orbis?

Philo. It is the very same, and Proclus describeth it in these wordes.

Λοξὸς δὲ ἐςι χύχλος ὁ τῶν ιβ ζωδίων. αὐτὸς δὲ ἐκ τριῶν κύχλων παραλλήλων σιωέστηκεν, ὡν ὁι μὲυ τὸ πλάτος ἀφορίζειν λέγεται τῶ ζωδιαχῶ χύχλϖ,ὁ δὲ διὰ μέσων τῶν ζωδίων χαλεῖται.οὗτος δὲ ἐφάπτεται δύο χύχλων ἴσων χαὶ παραλλήλων,τῶ μὲυ θερινῶ τροπιχῶ χατὰ τὴν τῶ χαρχίνϖ πρώτην μοῖραν, τῶ δὲ χειμερινῶ τροπιχῶ χατὰ τλώ τϖ ἀεγοχέρωτος πρώτλω μοῖραν.τὸ δὲ πλάτος τϖ Ζωδιαχϖ χύχλϖ ἐςὶ μοῖρα ιβ. λοξὸς δὲ χέχληται ὁ ζωδιαχος χύχλος,διὰ τὸ τέμνειν τὰς παραλλήλϖς χύχλϖς.

Circulus autem obliquus est zodiacus, qui duodecim signa continet, ip-

net, ipſeque ex tribus circulis parallelis conſtituitur : quorũ duo la-
titudinẽ eius definiunt, tertius vero per media ſigna ducitur. Hic at-
tingit duos circulos æquales & parallelos, nẽpe Aeſtiualem tropicũ
in prima parte Cancri, & Hiemalem in prima parte Capricorni. La-
titudo autem Zodiaci eſt partium duodecim, & dicitur obliquus hic
circulus, propterea quod parallelos ſecat circulos.

The crokyd, oblique, or thwarte circle, is called the Zodiacke,
whiche in it conteyne the. xij. Signes, and is made of thre parallele cir
cles, of whiche two do conteyne in them the bredth, and latitude: the
third*do deuide the Signes equally in the myddes. This Zodiack, ex=
tendith vnto two equidiſtant circles, or paralleles. That is to ſay the
ſomer tropike, in the beginning of Cancer: and the winter in the be=
ginning or firſt degree of Capricorne. The latitude and bredth of the
Zodiack is. xij. degrees, and it is called thwarte or croked, becauſe it
croſſeth the parallele circles.

*This lyne is
called the e=
cliptick, becau
ſe in it is the
cõtinual cour=
ſe of the Sõne
and that all
Eclypſes as
well of him as
of the mone
can not be but
in this lyne.

And here you muſt note for eſchewing further error, that
th' author menith by croſſinge the parallele circles, that
the zodiack goeth ouerthwarte them, and not rightly as
th' equinoctiall, and the right Horizont doth.

the ſphere

Spoud. And this circle, is deuided into. xij. equall
partes whiche you call ſignes.

Philo. You haue truly ſpoken: yea and euery ſigne, is
deuided into. xxx. partes, whiche they call degrees: and
euery degree, into. lx. minutes. &c. But this ſerueth
rather for Aſtronomers.

What a ſigne
is.

What a degre
is.

Spoud. By your wordes J gather the lengthe of a degree to be the. 360. parte of the heauen (for. xij. tymes
30. maketh. 360.) and not any determined, or appointed
meaſure, as a yarde, a forlong, a myle. &c.

What a mi-
nute is.

Philo. Vnto this circle and th' equinoctiall, al the mouing of the Planetes, and fixed ſtarres is referred. For
by them we fynde out their longitude, latitude, and alſo
                    D.   the eleua-

th'eleuation of ether poles, whiche is so necessary in this arte, as without it you shall little or nothing profite. But nowe I wyll set before your eyes the signes, with their names in Greke, Latine, and Englishe, adding also certaine characters of euery one of them, which the Astrologians do vse both in their wryting, also in their instrumentes.

	1	2	3	4	5	6
Septemtrional signes.	Κριὸς,	Ταῦρος,	Δίδυμοι,	Καρκίνος,	Λέων,	Παρθένος.
	Aries,	Taurus,	Gemini,	Cancer,	Leo,	Virgo,
	Rāme,	Bulle,	Twinnes,	Crabbe,	Lion,	Virgyn,
	♈	♉	♊	♋	♌	♍
	7	8	9	10	11	12
Meridionall signes.	Χηλάι,	Σκόρπιος,	Τοξότης,	Αιγόκερος,	Ὑδροχοος,	Ἰχθῦς,
	Libra,	Scorp.	Sagitta,	Capricor.	Aquari.	Pisces,
	Balaū.	Scorpiō,	Archer,	Goate.	watermā.	Fishes.
	♎	♏	♐	♑	♒	♓

Spou.   These names I haue often red in Homer, Sophocles, and other greke Poetes: and the latin, in Virgil, Ouide, Horace, Palingenius, and euery other Poet wel neare do make of them mencion: and I do perceiue th'use of this circle to be very expediēt. For of it consisteth the quantitie of the yeare, the .iiij. tymes of the same, as the Spring, Somer, Haruest, Wynter. But I perceiue also other configurations, and formes, as well out of the zodiacke, as also in it. And the Poetes make mētion of many of them, as Charles wayne, the Dragō, Bootes, Th'egle, the flieng Horse, the seuen Starres, the great Dog, and others: of whiche you make no mention.

The vse of the zodiack.

Philo.   No, nether do I intende, lest that I shall seme to espie a mote in an other, and not a beame in mine own eye. For I wyll digresse as litle as possible I may, frō our

A Table

A TABLE OF MANY NOTABLE FIXED STERRES VVITH THER TREVV LONGITVDE, LATITVDE, AND DECLINATON, faithfully rectified vnto the yeare of our Lorde. 1559.

The names in Englyshe	The names in Latine	The names in Greke	The Longitude			The Latitude			Declination and Magni.			
			S	D	M	D	M	P	D	M	P	M
The Whales backe	Dorsum Cæti,		♈	6	6	15	40	M	12	11	M	2
The Whales belly	Venter Cæti.		♈	16	2	20	0	M	12	20	M	2
Aries horne.	Cornu Arietis.		♈	27	42	7	20	S	17	19	S	3
The Rammes head.	Caput Arietis.		♉	1	46	10	0	S.	21	16	S	3
The Bulles eye.	Oculus Tauri.	Λαμπαδίας	♊	3	42	5	10	M	15	42	S	1
Orions left foote.	Orio. pes siniss.		♊	10	12	31	30	M	9	14	M	1
Orions left shoulder.	Orion. hu. sini.		♊	11	26	17	30	M	4	37	S	2
First in Orions gyrdle.	Cing. Orio. pri.		♊	16	22	24	20	M	1	19	M	2
Second in Orions gyrdle.	Cing. Orio. se.		♊	18	22	24	50	M	1	49	M	2
Orions right shoulder.	Orio. hu. dex.		♊	23	6	17	0	M	6	18	S	1
The great Dogge.	Canis Maior.	Σείριος	♋	8	42	39	10	M	15	50	M	1
The lesser Dogge.	Canis Minor.	προχύων	♋	20	12	16	10	M	6	4	S	1
Brightest in Hydra.	Lucida Hydræ.		♌	21	2	20	30	M	4	47	M	2
The Lions neck.	Ceruix Leonis.		♌	23	16	8	30	S	21	59	S	2
The Lions harte.	Regulus.	Βασιλίσκος	♌	23	32	0	10	S	14	3	S	1
The Lions back.	Dorsum Leonis		♍	5	16	13	40	S	22	31	S	2
The Lions Tayle.	Cauda Leonis,		♍	15	32	11	50	S	16	49	S	1
The Crowes head.	Caput Corui.		♎	5	0	19	40	M	19	53	M	3
The Crowes ryght wyng.	Ala dextra Cor.		♎	9	36	14	50	M	17	8	M	3
The Virgins Spike.	Spica Virginis.	Στάχυς	♎	17	42	2	0	M	4	54	M	1
Betwixt Bootes thyghes.	Inter cox. Boo.		♎	18	6	19	40	S	22	9	S	1
South Ballaunce.	Lanx Merid.		♏	9	2	0	40	S	13	44	M	2
North Ballaunce.	Septemtriona.		♏	13	12	8	30	S	7	33	M	2
The Scorpions hart.	Cor Scorpij.	Ἀντάρης	♐	3	42	4	0	M	24	47	S	2
Hercules Head.	Caput Herculis		♐	8	42	37	30	S	15	20	S	3
The Serpentes head.	Caput Ophi.	Κεφάλη ὀφιόυχȣ	♐	15	52	36	0	S	14	7	S	3
The Egle.	Aquila.	Ἀετός	♑	24	52	29	10	S	7	27	S	2
Capricornes Tayle.	Cauda Capri.		♒	17	22	2	10	S	14	13	M	3
In Aquarius legge	Crus Aquarij.		♓	2	20	7	30	M	15	52	M	3
Pegasus shoulder.	Hu. Pegasi.		♓	17	42	29	40	S	13	0	S	2

first inſtitution. But J wil geue you here a table of many notable fixed ſtarres, which are profitable for the trieng out of the latitude of any country and place.

Spoud.　This table ſeruith vnto ſmal vſe (if my authors deceiue me not) onleſſe that J haue in lyke ſorte the declination of them.

Philo.　You ſaye ryghtly, and to ſatiſſie your expectation, J wyll alſo place here a table of declination of th'eclipticke lyne from th'equinoctiall, whiche ſhall extende vnto. 23. digrees. 28. minutes, the trew declination of the ſonne, of this our age.

Spoud.　J pray you ſir, what call you the declination of the ſonne, or other planet and ſterre?

Philo.　Jt is no other thing then the diſtaunce of anye ſterre from th'equinoctial vnto his true place in the zodiack. And here marke that euery ſterre hath two declinations, the one is hauing ther courſe in the zodiack frō the beginning of Aries, vnto th'ende of Virgo, and they are North frō th'equinoctial. Th'other from the beginning of Libra, vnto th'ende of Piſces, and they are ſaid to haue their declination ſouth from th'quinoctiall.

Euery Planet haue two declinations.

Spoud.　haue this declination of the ſonne, bene alway one, or it doth varie?

Philo.　J wyll ſhewe you, in the tyme of Ptolomæus as (his workes do teſtiſie) the ſonnes greateſt declination from th'equinoctiall was. xxiij. degrees. lj. minutes, and xxx. ſecondes. Almæon found it. xxiij. degrees. xxxiij. mynutes, and. xxx. ſecondes. Iohannes de monte Regio, tried it to be. 23. and but. 30. minutes. And George Pour bachius

The diuerſitie of the Sonnes declinatiō, frō Ptolomæus time, vnto our age.

bachius.23.degr.&.28.mi.which agreeth with our time

Spoud. This diuerſitie of obſeruatiõ, may ariſe rather
of the inſtrumentes not exactly made, then that he do ſo
vary in his declination.

Philo. Nay verely. I attribute the cauſe here of vnto
that mouing of the heauẽ which is called of Tebitius &
Alfonſus, motus trepidationis.

Spoud. How may J finde this varietie of declination,
by myne owne diligence.

Philo. Although it vary not in a mans lyfe any thing
ſenſible, yet becauſe you may both know the obſeruing of
it exactly and alſo teache other that hereafter ſhal lerne
as you are now inſtructed your ſelfe: I wil in fewe wordes
open the whole labour. Take a quadrant (the making of
whiche you ſhal ſee among the other inſtrumentes) and
and ſet it directly vpright vpon ſome playne in the meridian lyne (the finding of whiche you ſhal ſee in the next
treatiſe) and is here marked A. B. as alſo C. A. do re
preſent, the zenit or verticall point, then rayſe vp and
downe the ruler (hauing two ſight holes made in it) vnto the ſonne, whan as he is in the meridian line : and obſerue diligẽtly that height, in the circle of degrees noted
in your quadrant, frõ B. to C. the.xi.or.xii. day of Decẽ-
ber, which is B. D. vntill you finde he goeth no lower:
and againe in like caſe the.xi.or. xij. of Iune, vntyll you
perceiue he increaſeth nothinge in height, and is noted
here B. E. and ſo the diſtaunce of D. E. is the diſtaunce
of the. ij. tropick Circles.

How to finde out by Inſtru-ment the Son-nes Declinatiõ

Spoud. What meane you by thoſe tropick circles?

D. iij.　　　　　　Phi.

Philo.   *You shall knowe, our conclusion ended. This distaunce in our dayes is founde. 46. degrees. 56. minu-*

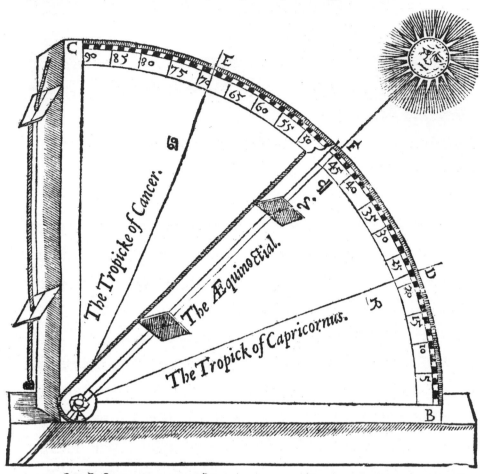

tes, which beyng parted in two equall parts, & reconed from th'Equinoctiall. B . F. sheweth the Sonnes greatest declination Northwarde from the forsaid Circle, 23. degrees. 28. minutes. And in like case Southwarde in Winter. And thus shall you alwaies find his declination.

Spoud.   *This rule will I put in practise whan the tyme of the yeare doeth insewe.*

Phil.   *Well now behold this table of Declinatiõ, which shall serue thy vse more largely thẽ Orontius, or D. Recordes Table: & is not so proplixe, as E. Reignholdes.*

AT A-

of th'Ecliptike, in Degrees, Minutes, & Secōdes, from th'Equi.
noctiall, answeryng to the Sonnes greatest Declinatiō.23.Deg.28.Minu.

Degrees.		Aries. ♈ Libra. ♎			Differē.		Taurus. ♉ Scorpius. ♏			Differē.		Gemini. ♊ Sagittarius. ♐			Differē.			
Deg.	Mi.	Deg.	Mi.	Se.	Mi.	Se.	Deg.	Mi.	Se.	Mi.	Se.	De.	Mi.	Se.	Mi.	Se.	De.	Mi
0	0	0	0	0	0	0	12	14	48			20	36	15			30	0
0	20	0	8	41			12	21	17			20	40	2			29	40
0	40	0	17	22			12	29	6			20	43	47			29	20
1	0	0	26	2			12	26	12	14	1	20	47	29			29	0
1	20	0	34	43			12	43	16			20	51	8			28	40
1	40	0	43	24			12	50	18			20	54	45			28	20
2	0	0	52	4			12	57	19			20	58	20			28	0
2	20	1	0	45	1	9	13	4	17			21	1	52	22	1	27	40
2	40	1	9	26			13	11	14			21	5	21			27	20
3	0	1	18	6			13	18	10			21	8	48			27	0
3	20	1	26	46			13	25	3			21	12	12			26	40
3	40	1	35	25			13	31	54			21	15	34			26	20
4	0	1	44	5			13	38	42	15	6	21	18	54			26	0
4	20	1	52	43			13	45	28			21	22	11			25	40
4	40	2	1	22	2	19	13	52	13			21	25	25			25	20
5	0	2	10	1			13	58	57			21	28	37			25	0
5	20	2	18	39			14	5	37			21	31	46			24	40
5	40	2	27	17			14	12	16			21	34	53			24	20
6	0	2	35	53			14	18	53			21	37	58			24	0
6	20	2	44	30	3	9	14	25	27			21	40	59			23	40
6	40	2	53	6			14	31	59	16	0	21	43	58			23	20
7	0	3	1	42			14	38	31			21	46	56			23	0
7	20	3	10	17			14	44	59			21	49	51			22	40
7	40	3	18	52			14	51	25			21	52	42			22	20
8	0	3	27	27			14	57	50			21	55	31			22	0
8	20	3	36	0	4	8	15	4	12			21	58	17			21	40
8	40	3	44	33			15	10	32			22	1	1			21	20
9	0	3	53	6			15	16	49			22	3	43			21	0
9	20	4	1	38			15	23	4			22	6	22			20	40
9	40	4	10	9			15	29	18			22	8	59			20	20
10	0	4	18	40			15	35	30	17	2	22	11	33	23	1	20	0
10	20	4	27	10	5	6	15	41	39			22	14	4			19	40
10	40	4	35	38			15	47	46			22	16	33			19	20
11	0	4	47	7			15	53	51			22	19	0			19	0
11	20	4	52	34			15	59	53			22	21	24			18	40
11	40	5	1	1			16	5	53			22	23	45			18	20
12	0	5	9	27			16	11	52			22	26	4			18	0
12	20	5	17	51	6	4	16	17	47			22	28	20			17	40
12	40	5	26	15			16	23	41			22	30	34			17	20
13	0	5	34	39			16	29	33			22	32	45			17	0
13	20	5	43	1			16	35	22	18	1	22	34	54			16	40
13	40	5	51	23			16	41	9			22	37	0			16	20
14	0	5	59	43			16	46	53			22	39	3			16	0
14	20	6	8	2	7	0	16	52	35			22	41	4			15	40
14	40	6	16	21			16	58	15			22	43	2			15	20
15	0	6	24	39			17	3	53			22	44	59			15	0
15	20	6	32	55			17	9	28			22	46	52			14	40
		Pisces. ♓ Virgo. ♍			Diffe.		Aquarius. ♒ Leo. ♌			Diffe.		Capricorn ♑ Cancer ♋			Differ.		Degries.	

THE SECOND PARTE OF THE

Table of Declination of th'ecliptick, from th'Equinoctiall.

Degrees		Aries ♈ Libra ♎			Differë		Taurus ♉ Scorpius ♏			Differë		Gemini ♊ Sagittarius ♐			Differë			
Deg.	Mi.	Deg.	Mi.	Se.	Mi.	Se.	Deg.	Mi.	Se.	Mi.	Se.	De.	Mi.	Se.	Mi.	Se.	De.	Mi
15	20	6	32	55			17	9	28			22	46	52			14	40
15	40	6	41	10			17	15	1			22	48	43			14	20
16	0	6	49	25			17	20	33			22	50	31			14	0
16	20	6	57	37			17	26	2			22	52	17			13	40
16	40	7	5	49	8	5	17	31	29			22	54	0			13	20
17	0	7	14	1			17	36	52			22	55	41			13	0
17	20	7	22	11			17	42	13	19	4	22	57	18			12	40
17	40	7	30	19			17	47	33			22	58	54			12	20
18	0	7	38	26			17	52	50			23	0	28			12	0
18	20	7	46	31			17	58	4			23	1	59			11	40
18	40	7	54	36			18	3	16			23	3	25			11	20
19	0	8	2	41	9	8	18	8	26			23	4	52			11	0
19	20	8	10	43			18	13	33			23	6	15			10	40
19	40	8	18	44			18	18	38			23	7	36			10	20
20	0	8	26	44			18	23	41			23	8	53			10	0
20	20	8	34	42			18	28	42			23	10	8			9	40
20	40	8	42	38			18	33	40			23	11	20			9	20
21	0	8	50	34	10	0	18	38	35			23	12	31			9	0
21	20	8	58	28			18	43	28	20	0	23	13	39			8	40
21	40	9	6	21			18	48	19			23	14	44			8	20
22	0	9	14	13			18	53	7			23	15	46			8	0
22	20	9	22	2			18	57	53			23	16	45			7	40
22	40	9	29	50			19	2	36			23	17	43			7	20
23	0	9	37	38	11	0	19	7	18			23	18	38			7	0
23	20	9	45	23			19	11	57			23	19	30			6	40
23	40	9	53	7			19	16	33			23	20	20			6	20
24	0	10	0	49			19	21	7			23	21	7			6	0
24	20	10	8	29			19	25	38			23	21	51			5	40
24	40	10	16	8			19	30	7			23	22	33			5	20
25	0	10	23	47			19	34	33			23	23	13			5	0
25	20	10	31	23			19	38	56			23	23	50			4	40
25	40	10	38	57			19	43	18			23	24	25			4	20
26	0	10	46	29	12	6	19	47	38			23	24	56			4	0
26	20	10	53	59			19	51	55	21	1	23	25	25			3	40
26	40	11	1	29			19	56	9			23	25	52			3	20
27	0	11	8	58			20	0	21			23	26	17			3	0
27	20	11	16	25			20	4	30			23	26	39			2	40
27	40	11	23	48			20	8	37			23	26	58			2	20
28	0	11	31	10	13	1	20	12	41			23	27	14			2	0
28	20	11	38	30			20	16	42			23	27	28	24	0	1	40
28	40	11	45	49			20	20	41			23	27	39			1	20
29	0	11	53	7			20	24	39			23	27	48			1	0
29	20	12	0	22			20	28	34			23	27	54			0	40
29	40	12	7	36			20	32	26			23	27	58			0	20
30	0	12	14	48			20	36	15			23	28	0			0	0
		Pisces ♓ Virgo ♍			Diffe.		Aquarius ♒ Leo ♌			Diffe.		Capricorn ♑ Cancer ♋			Differ.		Degries.	

Spoud. *J pray you learne me th'yſe of this table.*

Philo. *That J wyll reſerue vnto his neceſſary place?*

Spou. *Then or we procede any further, ſhow me what the poles of the zodiake be, for euery circle haue his proper poles: yea and whether they be all one with the poles of th'equinoctiall.*

Philo. *J will fulfill your requeſt. The poles of the zodiacke, do muche differ from the poles of th'equinoctiall, as you may eaſely perceiue by this figure here placed. In which I haue made C. H.*

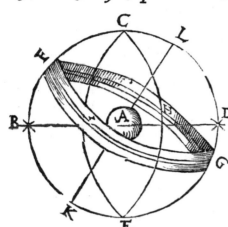

E. I. for th'equinoctial: F. H. G. I. for the zodiacke, and A. for th'earth. Now if I make B. D. the poles of th'equinoctiall as they muſt nedes be: thē can thei not be the poles of the zodiack, as herafter you ſhal heare, but K. L. being the endes of th'axe tree of the ſayd zodiack, ſhall be the poles.

Spoud. *J vnderſtande your mynde. Wyll you now declare vnto me the meanyng of the two tropikes, of which you lately made mencion.*

Philo. *Yea and that right gladly, vſing Proclus autho ritie as in the other circles whiche ſaith.*

Θερινὸς δὲ τροπικὸς κύκλος ᷞἐστὶν ὁ βορειότατος, τῶν ὑπὸ τῦ ἡλίῦ γραφομίμ́ων κύκλων. ἐφ᾽ ᷞὀυ γενόμμ́νος ὁ ἥλιος τίὼ θερινὴν τροπὴν ποιεῖται. ἐν ᷞἧ, ἡ μεγίστη μὴ́ πασῶν τῶν ἐν τῷ ἐνι-αυτῷ ἡμέρα, ἐλαχίστη δὲ ἡ νὺξ γίνεται. μετὰ μ̀δ́ὺ τοι τίὼ θερινὴν τροπὴν, ὀυκ ἔτι πρὸς τὰς ᷞἄρκτῦς παραδ́ὺ́ων ὁ ἥλιος θεωρεῖται, ἀλλ᾽ ἐπὶ θάτερα μέρη τρέπεται τῦ κόσμῦ: δ᷅ιὸ κέκληται τροπικός.

What the ſom mer tropick is.

Æſtiuus Tropicus, ē circulus oīm quos ſol deſcribit, ꝓxime Septē-triones vergens, in quo cum fuerit Sol, reuerſionem æſtiuam facit: Vbi omniũ totius anni lōgiſſima dies, nox verobreuiſſima habetur. Nam poſt reuerſionē æſtiuam, non vltra ad ſeptétriones ꝓgredi Solé videris, sed ad alteram mũdi partem reuerti: vnde circulus hic, Tropicus appellatus est.

The Somer Tropick (saith Proclus) is the most northely circle which the Sonne describeth, in to whiche whan as he enterith, it is the longest daye, and shortest nyght in all the yeare. For after this somerlye reuerting, the Sonne is not perceiued to decline farther North, but directly to the contrary coost: for which cause this circle is called a tropike (or circle of reuerting and turning back.)

Spou.   And what calleth he th'other tropicke?

Philoni.   The wynter tropike or circle of retorning from the South: as these his wordes folowyng do testifie.

Χειμερινὸς δὲ τροπικὸς κύκλος ἐστὶν ὁ νοτιώτατος τῶν ὑπὸ τῦ ἡλίυ γραφοιθύων κύκλων κατὰ τιὼ ὑπὸ τῦ κόσμυ γινοιθύην περιστροφήν. ἐφ᾽ οὗ γενύιθρος ὁ ἥλιος τὴν χειμερινιὼ τροπὴν ποιεῖται. ἐν ᾗ, ἡ μεγίστη μὴ πασῶν τῶν ἐν τῷ ἐνιαυτῷ νὺξ ἐπιτελεῖται, ἐλαχίστη δὲ ἡμέρα. μετὰ μὴ τοι τὶω χειμερινὴν τροπὴν, ὀυκέτι πρὸς μεσημιβρίαν παραδεύων ὁ ἥλιος θεωρεῖται, ἀλλ᾽ ἐπὶ θάτερα μέρη τρέπεται τῦ κόσμυ, διὸ κέκλιται καὶ ὅυτος τροπικός.

Hyemalis vero tropicus circulus est omnium, quos Sol per mũdi conuersionẽ describit, maxime australis, in quẽ cũ sol puenerit hyemalem reuersionẽ facit: vbi maxima oĩm totius anni nox, dies vero minima conficitur. Nã post hyemalẽ reuersionẽ, sol vltra nõ pergit austrum versus, sed ad alterã mũdi partẽ reuertitur, vnde & huic quoq; circulo tropici nomen inditum est.

The tropick of winter, is the furdest south circle of al other that ỹ sonne by the tournynge of the world doth describe: into whiche whan he doth enter, he maketh his wynterly retorne backwarde, at which season it is the lõgest night in all the yeare, and shortest day. For after this retourne, the sonne goth not further south, but doth approche to the contrary part of the worlde: for whiche cause, this circle also was called a tropicke circle.

Spo.   Proclus here meaneth (as by the repetitiõ of his wordes I gather) that these two tropikes, ar as it wer the boũdes, & lẽgth of the Sonnes iournay. For goyng from the Sommer tropicke in the begynning of the Crabbe, he directeth his course in the zodiacke towardes Libra in th'equinoctiall: and so leuing it, draweth vnto the Wynter Tropicke in the begynnyng of the Goate, beyonde which he can not goe, but retourneth backward agayne,

vntyll

What the winter Tropick is.

vntyll he cum to the head of the Ramme.

Philo. Jt is so, and by these wordes you maye also gather, that the .iiij. tymes of the yeare, Spryng, Sommer, Haruest, and Wynter, haue their beginnig in these .iiij. pointes (that is) the two Æquinictiall pointes, and the tropickes.

The foure tymes of the yeare whereof they take beginning.

Spoud. You haue here iust occasion to speake of the diuersitie of daies, and nightes, and it please you.

Philo. Yet that shalbe omittid vntill we make mentiõ of clymates, and the paralleles : and at this present wyll speake of these circles whiche do deuide as wel Th'equinoctiall, as also the zodiacke, into .iiij. equall partes : so that the Sonne being in any of them do make one of the forsayde tymes.

Spou. These circles also are necessarye, but what are their names?

Philo. They are called Colures, of which th'one is drawen by the beginning of Aries and Lybra, and of that is named th'quinoctiall Colure, and th'other by the beginning of cancer, and Capricorne, and called therof the solstitiall Colure, and are definid of Proclus in this maner.

Διὰ τῶν πόλων δὲ εἰσὶ κύκλοι ὑπό τίνων κόλουροι προσαγορευόμ̣ͅνοι, οἷς συμβέβηκεν ὑπὸ τῶν ἰδίων περιφερειῶν τοὺς τῦ κόσμῦ πόλους ἔχειν. κόλῦροι δὲ κέκλͅνται, διὰ τὸ μέρη τινὰ ἀθεώρητα αὐτῶν γίνεσθαι. οἱ μͅν γͅρ λοιποί κύκλοι κατὰ τͼν περιστροφὴν τῦ κόσμῦ ὅλοι θεωρῦνται τῶν δὲ κολούρων κύκλων μέρη τινὰ ὅτι ἀθεώρητα, τὰ ἀπὸ τῦ ἀνταρκτικῦ ὑπὸ τὸν ὁρίζωντα ἀπολαμβανόμͅνα. γͅάφονται δὲ ὗτοι οἱ κύκλοι διὰ τῶν τροπικῶν σημείων, κͅ εἰς μέρη .λ. ἴσα διαιρῦσι τὸν διὰ μέσων τῶν ζωδίων κύκλον.

What the two coloures are.

Per polos mūdi ducūtur circuli, quos aliqui coluros vocāt: quibus accidit, vt in sua circūferétia polos mundi habeāt. Coluri vero dicti sūnt, ppterea quod eorū partes quædā non videātur. Nã reliqui circuli per mūdi cõuersioné toti cernutur colurorū vero partes quædam
nunquàm

nunquàm videntur, eæ scilicet, quas sub horizonte nobis condit circulus Antarcticus. Cæterum ducūtur hii circuli, per puncta tropico-
rum , & in partes duas æquales diuidunt eum circulum , qui est in
zodiaci medio.

There are circles drawen by the poles (whiche some men call) Co-
lures:and conteine in their circumference the Poles of the worlde, &
they be named Colures, or trunckid circles, for this consideration, be-
cause that some partes of them are not at any tyme sene. The other
circles by the turninge of the worlde are all apparantly seene : but
some partes of the colures , be neuer decernyd. Suche are these partes
as are vnder our Horizont in the circle Antarctike.These circles also
are drawne by the.ij.tropike pointes,deuiding the eclipticke in two
equall partes.

Spoud. *Is there yet more circles to be obserued?*

Philoni. *Onely Th'arctike,and Antarctike circle re-*
mayneth,and then you haue learned all suche circles of
What the arc
ticke circle is.
the sphere , as shall serue for our purpose at this present,
and therfore I wyll make definition of them.

Αρκτικὸς μὲν ἐστι κύκλος ὁ μέγιστος τῶν ἀεὶ θεωρουμένων κύκλων,ὁ ἐφαπτόμενος τῶ ὁρίζοντος κατθ ἐν σημεῖον,καὶ ὅλος ὑπὲρ γην ἀπολαμβανόμενος. ἐν ᾧ τὰ κείμενα τῶν ἄστρων ὄυτε
δύσιν, ὄυτ' ἀνατολὴν ποιεῖται,ἀλλὰ δἰ ὅλης τῆς νυκτὸς περὶ τὸν πόλον στρεφόμενα θεωρεῖται.

Arcticus circulus omnium maximus orbiū , qui nobis semper videntur,qui attingens vno puncto Horizontem,totus extat super ter-
ram:inter quē inclusa sydera,nequè oriuntur,nequè occidūt,sed tota
nocte mundi lustrare polum spectantur.

The Arctike circle is the greatest of suche circles as do at all times
totally apeare : whiche touchinge in one pointe onlye the Horizont,
is in all partes aboue th'earth.And all sterres with in this circle inclu-
ded,do nether rise,nor yet set,but turne round about the pole, all the
longe nyght.

Spoud. *What calleth Proclus the antarctike circle?*
What the An
tarctickcircle
is.
Philo. *I wyll repete his wordes.*

Ανταρκτικὸς δε ἐστι κύκλος ἴσος καὶ παράλληλος τῶ αρκτικῶ, καὶ ἐφαπτόμενος τῶ ὁρίζοντος
κατθ ἐν σημεῖον,καὶ ὅλος ὑπὸ γῆν ἀπολαμβανόμενος:ἐν ᾧ τὰ κείμενα τῶν ἄστρων διὰ παντὸς
ἡμιν ἐστι ἀόρατα.

Antarcticus circulus,est ac parallelus æqualis Arctico orbi , attingés
Horizótem vno puncto,& totus sub terra conditus:intra quem , có-
plexa sydera nunquàm à nobis cernuntur.

And may aptly be translated into English as foloweth.

The

The Antarctike circle, is an equall parallele with the circle Arctick, touching the Horizōt in one only point, and is totally vnder the Earth: & the Sterres whiche are within it comprehended, do neuer rise aboue the Horizont.

Spou. Yet I haue harde, that such as inhabite the South partes of Spaine, & in Calecut, Guinea, & diuers other cūtreis, do see many goodly & bright Serres, yea & the southe Pole figured with sterres like à Crose.

Phi. It is as you haue said. But of that we will speake in the treatise of Nauigatiō, & to retorne to Proclus, he meaneth not that the Antartictick Circle & pole of the same is vnder the Horizōt to all men: but to vs that are on this side th'Equinoctiall, & therefore it is spoken no lesse trewly, then pleasantly of the swete Poët Virgilius.

Hic, Vertix nobis semper sublimis, at illum   *Lib. 2. Geor.*
     Sub pedibus, Stix atra Videt, manesq; profundi.
The northe Pole, Still we haue in sight:
     But vnder th'Earth, the South sterre right.

Spou. And what is the Axe tree, & poles of this circle? Philoni. The same, that are of th'Equinoctiall, & the two tropike circles. For seyng th'Equinoctiall, the ij.tropikes, & the circles Arctike, & Antarctike, be equididistant paralleles (as Proclus affirmeth) it must thē of necessitie folow, that they are reuolued, & turned vpon the same Poles, & haue all one Axe tree. Theodosius also confirmeth the same in these wordes.

Ἐν σφαίρα, ὅι παράλληλοι κύκλοι περὶ τοὺς αὐτοὺς πόλους ἐισίν.
In Sphæra, paralleli circuli circa eosdem polos sunt.   *Li.2. Theor.*
In à Sphere the parallele or equidistant Circles, haue all one Pole.

But I will not burden you (& especillye in à trewe cause) whiche suche graue authoritie, but giue you
E.j.   the

the figure of thefe .vj. laft Circles , & then procede further herein. In this figure is fet all the .v. Paralleles ,the
ij. Colures , & the Zodiake. And firft B.D. is the
Equinoctiall. E. F. the
tropike of Cancer. H. G.
the tropike of Capricorne.
K. M. the Circle Arctike,
& L. I. the circle Antarticke, A. B. C. D. the
Solftitial colure, A. N. C.
O. th' Equinoctial colure, E.G. the Zodiake, & A.C. the
Axe tree, which goeth thorow the Center of th' Earth directly, & endeth at the Poles.

Spoud.   I muft confeffe the wordes of Theodofius, &
Proclus, to be trew: but yet mufinge with my felfe, I can
not conceiue by what reafon this Axe tre fhould ftey the
Earth. And it ftandyng fixed, the heauens as well vnder
it, as alfo aboue th' Earth, fhould be turned, & reuolued
in like maner, as we fee: & I euer feare leſt th' Earth,
beynge fo heauie, & ponderous, as it is, fhould fall to the
other part of the Heauens, which is vnder it.

Philo.   I perceiue you are not yet free from the fond
imaginations of the groffe witted people , but yet you are
the more to be excufed, feyng Lactantius beynge fo learned à man, was fo folifhe (whether it fprong of petulancye, or ignoraunce, I knowe not) as to affirme the Heauens to be flat, & not to go vnder th' Earth.

Lactantius petulancie.

But

But now to your doubt, I answere: if God by his wōder-
full prouidence, & power, did not steye it in the place
where it is, there could be no axe tree whiche mighte su-
steine so vnknowen à burthen, & weighte: & therefore
you must rather imagine à streight line, to be the forsaid
axe tree, (as also the Circles of which we haue intreatid,
beyng voide of Latitude, and Profunditie) then to beleue any such circles, or yet axe tree to be in the Heaūes
visiblie:

Spoud.   I perceiue your meaning right well.

Philoni..   Nowe you haue learned what the vj.
great circles of the Sphere ar, as the Horizōt, the Meridian, th'Equinoctiall, the zodiake, th'Equinoctiall, &
the solsticiall Colures: as also the iiij. lesser Circles, which
are the tropicke of Cancer, the tropick of Capricorne, the
circle Articke, and the circle Antarticke.

Why sum Cir-
cles are called
greater, and
some lesser.

Spoud.   I haue so, I thank you sir. But for what cause
be the vj. called the greater Circles, & the iiij. the lesser?

Philo.   Iohn de Sacro Bosco, doeth answere your question in these, or like wordes. We call that à greater Circle of a Sphere (saith he) which beyng drawen in the cōpasse of the Sphere vpon his Center, do diuide it into two
equall portions : & that a lesser Circle, whithe beynge
drawen as th'other, do not diuide the Sphere into equall
partes, but inequall portiōs, such ar the iiij. lesser Circles.

Spou. If I shall for the better vnderstanding such thinges as herto are spoken, make a Sphere of Hopes, & applie your preceptes to the instrumēt, by what order maye
I gather the trew proportiō of one of them, to an other?

Philo.   Becauſe the tyme doth ſo faſte rõne, & I haue alſo other matters to intreate on: I wyll reſerue the making of the Sphere, vntyll I ſhewe you the cõpoſition of other inſtrumentes required in this Art, in my Organographie. But nowe for this preſent, let this figure (repreſentyng the forme of the Sphere, with all the principall Circles to it belõging) ſatisfie thine expectation.

Th'other part of the diuiſion of the worlde.

LINEA MERIDIANA

Spoud.   Then will it pleaſe you to take in hande the ſecõde part of your diuiſion of the worlde, for hitherto (if I be not diſceiued) ſtretcheth the declaratiõ of the heauenlye Region.

Piloni.   Trewe it is, for oure talke as yet either was of this regiõ, or els of thynges giuynge lyghte to the ſame : and now let vs conuerte oure ſtyle in like maner vnto th'Elemẽtary Region. This in it ſelfe, cõteineth the iiij. Elementes, Fyre, Aëre, Water, & Earth, (theſe are not corruptible) alſo whatſoeuer is cõteined within the circuit of the heauen of the Mone, as well bodies perſite, as alſo imperſite, made of the forſaide

Elementes

Elementes (the Latinistis call them) corpora mixta.

Spoud.   And wherfore are ther but iiij. Elementes?

Philo.   Aristotle doeth giue à sufficient reason: saying, there are so many Elementes as ther is combination, & mixture, of the simple and first qualities, which can be but foure: hoot, and drie, propre to the Fire: hoote and moiste, of th'Aëre: coulde and moist, which is resembled to the water: & could with drynes, to th'Earth. As for heate and couldnes, are so repugnaunt that ther can be no mixture of them: no more then of moisture & drynes. There is also an other reason made of Aristotle, taken of the diuersitie of motion, whiche J do at this time wyllingly ouer passe.

Why ther can be but iiij. Elementes.
Lib. 2. de generatione.

Lib. primo de Cœlo.

Spou. We are agreed of the number of th'Elementes, but what is theyr order, whiche of them is higher, and which of them lower?

Philo. That Element is higher then the rest, which is lyghtest, most fugitiue, and subtile. For it is a generall maior among Philosophers, that al light thynges cõtend vpwarde: & all grosse and poderous, to the Center of the Earth.   Spou. By this propositiõ J gather, that the Fyre beyng more subtyl than th'other thre, shal ascend aboue them, & be next the Globe of the Mone. For you said, that ther may be no place emptie, & void. And then next him the Aëre, then the Water, & laste of all th'Earth.

A generall maior.

The situation & place of th'Elementes.

Philo. It is in like order as you haue said. And the Fire, conteyneth in him the Aëre : Th'Aëre, in his compasse the Water : & the Water also doth cõpasse & inuirone

E.iij.   th'Earth

The Earth, not rounde about as th'other do, but in diuers parts, so that the water, & th'earth, rather make one vnifourme Globe: as this Figure here annexid doth plainely declare.

Spoud. Ther semeth in your description to be fiue distincte Regions, How may that be, seyng that ther are but iiij. Elemētes? Philo. Ther are as you haue saide, but the Äerie Regiō, is deuidid into

Th'Aere deuidid into thre Regions.

iij. parts, springing thorow Heate, and Colde: as the hier part of the Äere signified with A. being nere to the Orbe of the Fier, and is daylie caried about, (as Cometes and

Where Cometes and blasing Sterres are ingendred.

blasing Sterres ther ingendred, do apparantly declare.) and is made more hoote thē the middle Regiō is: againe, the lower region next vs, markid with C. is thorowe the reflextiō of the Sonne beames rebounding from th'earth also made hoote, therfore the middle region B. beynge voide of heate, is alway coulde: yea and so much the coulder, howe muche the heate is more vehement in th'other two regions.

Where Haile and Snow is ingendred.

Spou. Then in this middle region I suppose all Haile, Snow, and suche like is ingendrid.

Phil. It is so, but I let that passe, and intreate of th'use

of

of them, touching our firſt meanyng.

Spoud. Becauſe the Fire, and Aëre, ſhould ſeme litell to profit in this place, wil you ſomwhat ſpeake of the Water, and Earth?

Philo. Ĵ will ſpeake nothing of the Water (but referre it vntil we intreat of Ńauigatiõ) but only in this place, make mention of th'earth, and ſo depart vntill to morow.

Spou. And it weare not more for troblynge you, then any werines that Ĵ haue, Ĵ would wiſhe the day to be. x. daies in length, Ĵ haue receiued ſuche pleaſure in youre inſtructions. But ſence the Sonne ſumwhat declineth to the weſte Ocian, Ĵ will giue diligent eare vnto your wordes, for the ſhort time ther is yet remaining.

Phil. Ĵ reioyſe much to vnderſtand your feruent deſire to knowledge, which Ĵ will to my vttermoſt furder. And now touching th'Earth, conſider you that ſhe is loweſt of all Elementes: blacke, ponderous, and round, inuironid, and incloſed within th'other thre. She is called the mother of fruites, the rcote of all plantes, the noriſhe of lyuing creatures, the foundation of all buildinges, the ſepulchre of the dead, the Center of the beautifull frame of the world, the matter and ſubſtaunce of mans body, and the receptakle of heauenly influence. She is alſo garniſhed with fragrãt flowres, of Man, Beaſt, and Foule, inhabited, and comfortablie quickened by the noriſhing beames of the Sõne, Mone, Planetes, and fixed Sterres. But you ſhall note for all that here is ſpoken, that there is great controuerſie touching th'Earthes fourme : which muſt be deſcidid and put away, or we can ſafely procede

What th'Erth is.

Diuerſitie of opinions touching th'Erth his fourme.

E.iiij.   fur-

further. As th'opinions of those which affirme th'Earth
not to be rounde, like à Globe or Boule. Those that affirme it to be of pyller forme. Those that will not haue
it to be the Center of the heauen. Those that suppose the
Earth to moue: with other like. But the greatest of all, is
the errour of those that speake againste the roundnes of
th'Earth. Wherfore J will touche it principallye, whiche
thing done, th'other are manifest of them selues.

Spoud.   You enter into that question, in whiche of all
other J desire moste especiallie to be satisfied, for J also
am in that errour (if it be an errour to say th'earth is not
rounde.)   Philo. Bring forth suche
reasons than, as inforseth you so to iudge, and J will an-

An obiection,
against the
round fourme
of th'Earth.

swere them.   Spou. It semeth sufficient to
credit th'Earth not to be round, if we consider the greate
deepe valleis, that are in it: the Cities, Towres, Castels,
and Trees, with suche like placed vpon the face of the
Earth: but moste of all, the hougie and hie Mountaines,

These Hilles
are the grea-
test in all the
Earch.

and Hilles : Of whiche, some of them are supposed to be
60. miles in height. As the Hille in th'Iland Teneriffa,
(whiche Ptolomæus nameth one of the fortunate Ilandes) and is beyonde Hercules Pillers. Also an other in

*This is the fa
mous Hill of
which Poëtes
so muche in-
treate: in the
top of whiche
the Gentils
builded an aul
ter making to
Iuppiter Sa-
crifice.

Thessalia, called (of Solinus) Olimpus, * beyng of suche
height that the ashes (ther daies of Sacrifice beynge ended) remaine à whole yeare in the toppe of the same, not
moued with troublous tēpestes, or vehement blastes : but
thorow his great height, is free from all violence of windes. What shall J speake of the Hill Caucasus, which diuideth Albania & Colchis, from Sermatia (as doth appeare

peare in the seconde Table of Asia, in Ptolomæus Geographie) which Aristotle doth esteme to be of such hight,
that it may be sene at the mouth of the riuer mæotis. The
distaunce of which, is from the forsaid Hill. 620. English
miles. Moreouer you shall see no place, but either flat, or
els full of Hylles, Dales, Valeis, or suche like, whiche is
farre from à Globe forme, & figure.

Phil. Yet do all these wordes nothing coclude. Do you
not cosider, that the sight is deceiued in thinges from it,
farre distaunt. And therfore I will in fewe wordes answere you, that these Hilles, Mountaines, & Vallies,
are no more in quantitie (respect beyng had to the whole
Earth,) the the Pittes & holes of à rough polished Gu-
stone, to the stone: whiche although it be not smoth, yet it
argueth nothing lesse then this gunstone not to be roude,
& like a Globe in fourme: yea, & then the bodye of the
Earth beyng a rough stone, harde, & not so apt to be polished, as the body of the Water, doth remaine with such
vallies & Hilles as you haue saide, & in manye places
these vallies ar filled with water, to the more apt proportiõ of à Globe. Moreouer, Nature cosidering the necessitie of th'inhabitauntes in this Center, left suche fourme
vnto it as might for ther vse most coueniently serue.

Spou. For what cause suppose you th'Earth to be à
stone? Philo. If it were not à stone but
Sande, or Clay in substaunce, then the water being mixt
with it, they both should be cofounded in them selues: yea
& the hie Hilles, & Moutaines, (of which you made
mentiõ) shoulde sinke, & settle downe to the Center of
th'Earth

Th'answere to the first obiection.

Th'earth is a stone.

th'Earth: ſeynge, they are ſo ponderous, & heauie, &
not be ſuſtained, & borne vp as they are in the face of
th'Earth.   But for the further cõfirminge you in that,
which is ſpoken, aunſwere me. Jmagine there were à
great rounde trunke of Timber, which went thorow the
whole Earth directly by the Center, & then there were
à great heauie ſtone put in at this Trŭke: how farre ſuppoſe you this ſtone ſhould deſcende?

Spoud.   Vntill the center of th'Earth, & myddes of
the Trunke.   Philo. Jn like caſe, if th'earth
were not an hard, & ſtonie ſubſtaunce, but Clay or Sãde
(as to our ſightes doth appeare) theſe Hilles, & rockes
beyng much heauier then any ſtone, ſhould in like ſort go
to the Cẽter of th'earth. But haue you any other doubtes?

The 2. obiectiõ Spou.   Yea verely, & that is, th'Earth to be flat.

Philo. What prouoketh you ſo to iudge?

Spou. This reaſon, that th'Earth muſt be in forme moſt
agreable to the Heauens. And that the Heauẽs be flat,
J can proue by th'authoritie of Lactantius Firmianus.

Th'anſwere. Philoni. Jt is truely ſaid, that knowledge hath no ene-
mie but ignoraunce. There are nowe at theſe daies, no
ſmall numbre of Lactantius ſort, not ſcrupulous enemies
onely, but alſo Phyſicians, of whome J am aſhamed to
ſpeake, & they do contempne that knowledge (whiche
is the greateſt & ſueriſt token of Gods prouidence for
mankind) either by peruerſe interpreting the ſcripture,
or els of mere follie, diſpiſinge that, of whiche they neuer
taſted, & are vtterly ignorant in. But ſuch wer very ill
to be Judges, for they would condemne the man, or they
                                                        knew

knew the crime of whiche he were accused: but let that passe. As touchyng your opinion, that th' Earth is flat, J will proue it to be rounde from th' Eaſt to the Weſt : and in like maner, from the North, to the South.

Spou.　Then muſt I nedes graūt that it is in like ſorte rounde in all partes.

Philon. I wyll vſe the ſame argumētes that Cleomedes doeth. Jf th' Earth were flat, then the ſterres ſhould riſe at the ſame moment to vs, that they do to them whiche dwell in th' Eaſt parts of the world: & it ſhould be midday with vs, & them at one inſtaunt : yea & the ſame Starres ſhould ſet in the Weaſl in lyke maner with thē, and vs.　Spoud.　That they do not, I am moſt ſure: for at Alexādria, à citie in Egipt, it is day iij. houres ſooner then with vs: & night in like ſorte. Yea & at Compoſtell in Spaine (which is Weſt from vs) the daye begynneth with vs ſooner by one houre & a halfe, then with them : and is daye with them, after the Sonne is ſet with vs, in like ſort one houre, & xxx. minutes.

In lib. i. de Mundo.

Philo.　And all this cometh, becauſe th' Earth is round, cauſing vs & them not to haue one generall Horizont. The like reaſon is to be ſaid of the diuerſities of times, in the beginning of an Eclipſe, either of Sonne, or Mone. As for exāple, th' Eclipſe of the Mone, which was 1556. the 17. day of Noueber, at one of the clocke in the morning, with vs at Norwiche, (& for the moſte parte of Englande) which in the Horizont of Calicut, began at vij. of the clock. Jn like ſort, ther ſhall happē an Eclipſe of the Mone, in the yeare of Chriſt our ſauior. 1562. the

Example of ij. Eclipſes of the Moone.

16. day

16.daye of July, at two of the clocke, iiij.minutes in the morning: at which time she shalbe totallie darkened, & continew from the beginning to th'ende iij. houres, and yet th'inhabitauntes at Calicut, shall not see anye parte therof: whiche moste euidently sheweth the roundnes of th'Earth to be the cause, as this Figure here folowing do more plainely set out: in which, E. signifieth th'Earth: A. the East: C. the West: D. the verticall pointe for Norwich: & B. in like maner, the Zenit of Calicut. Wherby it is manifest that the Mone shalbe persitly seperated from the Sonne, or she shall appeare in the Horizŏt of Calicut. And yet we in England, & diuers other places East, shall se bothe beginning, & ende of her Eclypsing.

Spoud.　These are sufficiĕt probatiōs to declare th'Earth roŭd, frō th'East to the West: but by what argument can you shewe it to be also rounde from the South to the North?

Philo.　That is very easie to proue. For if th'Earth were flat from the South, to the North, then we should se the south Sterres vnder th'Earth: as well as those that be North alway in our sight. And againe, the Sonne, Mone, & Sterres, at midde day through the vniuersal yere, should be euer in one height: which also is false.

Spoud.　Yea, for J haue had practise of that thinge,

sayling

saylinge in à shippe, for we goynge from th'Equinoctiall
Line northwarde, did see the North, & south Poles,
equall with the Water. But directing our course more to
the north coast, & leauing th'Equinoctial, we reared the
north starre in short space. xij.degr. & at legth, 30.deg.
& loking south, we could not se the southe Pole, nor yet
many other sterres which in th'Equinoctial, were visible
to vs. Phi. Yea, & wher your north starre was eleuated xxx.degrees, your south Pole was xxx. degrees de-
pressed in like maner : But for the firmer fixynge it in
your memory, behould this Figure: in the which C.signi-

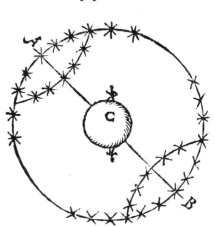

fieth both th'Earth, and
water, A.the north Pole,
& B.the south, therefore
if one go from B.to A(the
earth being roūd)he must
haue B. so muche vnder
him, as A is aboue his Horizōt. There are besides
these many, & sūdry rea-
sons, to proue this thing: which I may omit(as I suppose)
to you, which nede no lenger probatiō, in that whiche is
most manifest. Spo. Yet theis argumēts shall not onely
stay my mind inà trueth, but also with the same J shal cō
fute th'errors of other, if any shal spring about this matter. Phil. Then J wyll exhort you, wher these shall not
seme sufficient, you will gather more & stronger out of
Ptolomæus Almegiste, Cleomedes de mundo, Philo de
mundo, Aristotle, Erasmus Reignholt, Orontius,
F.j.   John

Ptolomæus.
Cleomedes.
Philo.
Aristotle.
E. Reignholt.
Orontius.

John

John de Sacrobosco, & oure countreyman master Recorde, which doeth almost repete all their argumentes, in the Castell of knowledge. And nowe behold the Type of the world, conteinyng in it, as well the heauenly Region, with suche Spheres, & Circles, as haue bene in sundry partes before set forth in this treatise: as also th'Elementarie region, comprehendyng the Fier, Aëre, Water, & Earth : in suche order & forme, as is cõsonant & agreyng both with Reason, Practise, and Authoritie of most approued authors. And for this time we will depart: for beholde the Sonne is gone to rest, & Hesperus do shewe in the West verie brighte, all other liuynge thinges also do apply them to take rest: therfore let vs go downe this Hill into the Citie, refreshyng our selues, & quickening memorie, & to morow I wil mete you in this same place agayne.

Spoud.   I thanke you hertly.   Philoni. Let me here & you can repete the summe of such thinges, as we haue taken in hande this day, as we walke downeward.

Spoud.   With à right good wyll.

1   Firste, you shewed me what Cosmographie was, what Geographie, and what Chorographie, yea, and wherein euery of them differeth from other.

2   Next, what the world was, with his partes (that is to saye) the Heauenly Region, & Elementary: with à briefe Discourse, touchinge the Partes, and order of the Heauenly Region.

3   Thyrdly, what a Sphere is, howe it is deuided into a Right, and Croked Sphere: And howe it differeth from a Cirle.

4　　*Forthly, what a Center was, what an Axe tree, what a Dia-meter, and of theyr difference.*

5　　*Fiftlye, of the Principall Circles whiche are saide to be in this Sphere. As the Horizont, Meridian, Æquinoctiall, Zodiake, two Colures, the two Tropickes, the Circles Arc-ticke, and Antarctick. Also that the Horizont, and Meri-dian Circles be stable, and without motiõ, with diuers other thinges herto belonging.*

6　　*Last, you proceded to the second part of the world, which is th'Elementarie Region: In which you refuted sundry opini-ons, touching the forme of th'Earth.*

Philo.　　*Nowe I perceiue bothe your apte nature in conceiuing such thinges as are spoken, & also your firme memory in reteining the same. Wherefore you shall en-courage me, to geue you further instructions.　But for this time I must bid you fare well.　　Spou.*

God preserue you, & graunt you life to ac-complishe your desire, in profiting your countrey, as you do entende.

Amen.

THE SECONDE BOOKE OF

the Cofmographicall Glaffe:in which is plainly expreffed the
Order, and Number, of Zones, Paralleles, and Climates. Alfo fun-
dry waies for th'exacte findyng out of the Meridiane Line:
The Longitude, & Latitude, of places:with many other
preceptes, belongyng to the making of a
Carte, or Mappe.

Spoudæus.

ORPHEVS THE God of dreames, with his flepie rodde, fo much this laft night frequented my companie, that (my bodye taking reft) my mind was much more bufilie traueling in fuch conclufions as I had learnid of Philoni- cus, thē it was in the time of his teaching. For fome time Morphêus fhewed me the Sonne, in the tropicke of Ca- pricorne, farre in the South, among the cloudye fkies, as he comenly is the.13.day of December: And next he ap- pered in th'Equinoctiall pointes, as it is the tenth daye of March, and the.14.of Septēb.willing me with great di ligēs to note that parallele circle. Shortly after the fone appeared in the tropicke of Cancer, in whiche place he is the.12.daye of Iune, caufing in our region the lōgeft day in the yere.& imediatly the time femed as it were mid- night,& Charles Wayne, with Bootes, & diuers other fterres, turned about the Pole. But as he wold haue ca- ried me about the heauēs, to haue fhewid me the North

Whā the Sōne is in the Tro- pick of Capri- corne.

In both Æqui noctiall poin- tes.

In the Tropick of Cancer.

F.iij.   Crowne

Crowne, ſtronge Hercules, Caſſiopeia, th' Egle, the flieng Horſe, mightie Orion, tbe two Dogges, & the famous, & great ſhippe Argo. &c. Mercury the meſſenger of the Godes came to my bedde ſide, & ſaide, Aurora did appeare, & Phebus with his goldē beames, was entred his chariot, minding to finiſhe his diurnall Arcke: ſo that it was à reproche for me, any lōger to play the ſluggard: declaringe more ouer that Philonicus was in the fildes. And ſurely I ſuppoſe no leſſe, but I ſhall not from him be longe abſent. I am iuſtly reprehended of Mercury, be-cauſe the time that is cōſumed with ſlepe more then na-ture requireth, is all loſt: for ther ſpring no profit therof, but ſicknes & diſquietnes, both of body & minde. But what is he that calleth Spoudæus, & beckneth with his hand? It is Philonicus. I will make ſpede to mete him.

Philon.   God ſaue you Spoudæus.

Spoud.   And you alſo, moſte hertilie I require the Gods: you know th' occaſiō (I truſt) of my reſorting into this place.   Philo.   For to be further inſtructed in the knowledge of Coſmographie.

what is taught in this ſeconde Booke.

Spoud.   It is verely my deſire, & ſpecially to know the Longitude, Latitude, & circuit of th' Earth, and of the diuiſiō of it into Climates, to know the meanyng of Zo-nes, & paralleles: to finde out the Meridiane line, the longitude & latitude of any place: becauſe they haue à ſinguler vſe in this Arte.

Philo.   You haue repeted matter ynough to cōſume this day in, & I wyll if tyme permitte, willingly ſatisfie your requeſt. But ſeynge this thinge doeth depende chiefly of

dimen-

dimention, & meaſuringe: it is requiſite to knowe that
firſt, yea & the principall partes of it.

Spou. Dimention is no other thing, then à lõgitude What Dimē-
tion is.
knowen, & practiſed: by which we maye in like maner,
meaſure th'vnknowẽ diſtaunce of places by the ſame experience. Philo. Trew it is. And there are thre
thinges only which may be meaſured. For either it is à
line, as Longitude: or els à Plat forme, as Latitude: or
laſt, à body, as thicknes, or profunditie.

Spoud. Glarianus hath the like ſaying, & Campanus
ſheweth wherof theſe three do ſpring, in this maner. A
point (ſaith he) is that which haue no partes, yet by the What a Point
is.
mouyng of it, à lyne is deſcribed. And a lyne, moued be- What a Lyne
is.
cauſe it hath length (beynge voide of breadth & depe-

A rounde plat forme.

nes) cã but deſcribe a plat
forme. This plat forme, is What a Plat
fourme is.
both a rounde plat forme,
& alſo a flatte, as in theſe
figures. And a plat forme
moued, becauſe it hathe
lẽgth & breadth, deſcri-
beth a Body, hauing both What a Body
is.
length, breadth, & depe-
nes. Philo. Hereto

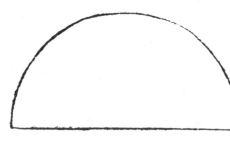

A plaine plat forme.

agreeth youre Pathway.
Now proced we further.
Becauſe in this Arte, the
chiefe meaſures we vſe, is
a Paſe, a Forlõg, a lequè,
E.iiij. a Mile,

a Mile, a Degree &c. J wil set before your eyes in this Table both the diuersitie of miles, & also their exacte length, placing a Barly corne (being the least measure) as the rule, wherby other measures shalbe tried. And like as progression is made from the least vnto the moste, as from a point, to a lyne: from a lyne, to a plat forme: and from a plat forme, to a body: euen so in the quantitie of measures, we do go frō a barly corne, to a finger breadth: from a finger breadth, to an vnch: frō an vnch, to an hād breadth: from an hand breadth, to a spanne: frō a spāne, to a fote: from a fote, to a pase: & so forth to a pearch, a furlong, a lequè, a mile, as in this Table is manifest and playne.

A Barly corne is the least mea sure, yet from it do all other mea sures procede, as	A Finger breadth,	Contey- ninge in it.	4 Barly cornes in thick (nes.
	An Vnche.		3 Fingers.
	A Hande breadth.		4 Fingers.
	A Spanne.		3 Hande breadth.
	A Fote.		4 Hande breadth.
	A Geomtricall Pase.		5 Fiue fote.
	An Englishe Pearche.		16 Fote & a halfe.
	A Furlonge.		125 Pase.
	An Englishe Furlonge.		660 Fote, or 132. Pase.
	A Leque.		1500 Pase.
	An Italian mile.		1000 pase, or 8. furlōgs
	A comon Germaine mile		32 Furlonges.
	An Englishe mile.		8 Furlonges.

There is also diuersitie what a Furlong should conteine in length, & it should appeare that Ptolomæus, Strabo, & Plinius, do not agree herin.

Lib.2.cap.23. Natura. hist.

Spou.   What call you this worde Furlong?

Philon.   That which the Grecians call Στάδιον, & Pli- nie name it stadium ἀπὸ τῆς στάσεος. That is, à statione. And it is vsurped, for a place where men exercise ther horse, ronnyng a rase, which length Plinie determineth to be 125. pases, or. 625. fote, by which reason. 8. of these fur- longes

longes do make an Italian or Englishe mile, which beyng multiplied by 4.makes.32. furlonges, the length of
a comon Germanie mile, I call it à common Germaine
mile, for that in Heluetia not obseruing any true distáce
in theyr iorneis, they vse 40.or. 50. furlōges for a mile.

Heluetian mi les.

Spou. Those are Robin Hodes miles as the prouerbe is.
Phi. There is also a diuers order in measure obserued,
as th'Ægiptians by signes : the Gretians by furlonges:
the Spaniardes, & French men by leques: the Italiãs,
Germaines, & Englishmen, by miles: which I thought
mete to declare, more for that it may further you in reading theyr workes, then that I entende to introduce in
place any of ther waies, but wil vse only th'English mile,
writing to Englishe men: the quantitie wherof as I said,
is 8.furlonges: euery furlonge conteining 132.pases: euery pase 5.fote: euery fote, 4.handbreadthes: euery hand
breadth, 4. fingers in thicknes : euery finger, 4. Barly
cornes rounde & dried. So that an Englishe mile conteineth in length.253440.Barly cornes, as by the rules
of Arithmetike, is manifest & plaine.

The quantitie of an Englishe mile.

Spoud. This semeth very straunge, yea rather incredible, yet surely to be trew, I am assured.
Philon.. You shall vnderstande matters, both more
straunge, & pleasaunt then this, which is founde out by
th'infalible rules of Arithmetik, & Geometrie: & now
procede we to our purpose, beginning with this word Lōgitude. Spoud. I take it for no other thinge then
the distaunce of à Starre, or part of à signe, from the beginning of Aries the first signe, in the Zodiake. As the
Virgines

Virgines spike , in the xvij. degree. xlij. minutes of Libra: is vj. signes, xvij. degrees, & xlij. minu. or 197. degrees. xlij. minu. from the head of Aries.

Longitude taken two waies

Philo.   That signification of Longitude, is vsed among th' Astronomers: but in Cosmographie it is otherwise. For they call the Longitude of any Region, the portion of th' Equinoctiall Circle, which is included betwixte the Canarian Ilandes, (in the West beyng the first degre of Longitude) & the Meridiane of the Regiō, that thou wilt describe. Such portiō of th' Equinoctiall in the middes of Englande (from the fornamed Ilandes) is about xxij. degrees. Spoud.   Then in describinge the face of th' Earth, Cosmographers do place the first degre of Longitude in the West fortunate Ilandes, & so proced thorow the whole face of the same, vntill they come to that place agayne.   Philo.   It is so as you say. So that the myddes of th' Earth is 180. degrees, from the West. Such are th' East Indians, & 360. is the furdest that one can be from the West.   Spou.   But could not the degrees of Longitude be accompted from some other parte of th' Earth, as well as from th' Iandes aforesaid?

Ptolomæus.

Philo.   Yes verely: but Ptolomæus the restorer of this Art, placed the first degree of Longitude in them, as the furdest point of the confines & boundes of Afrike, &

Hercules Pillers.

Europe: as the famous, & excellent pillers of Hercules (called of Diodorus Calpe, & Abyle) doth declare. The cause which moued Ptolomæus thus to do, you shal finde

In Prologo li. 2. Geographiæ

in his Geographie.   Spoud.   And is ther the like difference, betwixt Cosmographers & Astronomers cōcerninge

cerning the ſignification of the Latitude of à region, as
ther was in the Longitude?

Philo.   No verely: For they meane nothing els by the
Latitude of à region, but th' Arke, or portion of the Meridiane circle, conteined betwixt the Pole of the world,
& the Horizont of the ſame region.

Spou.   And is not this Latitude, reconed frõ th' Equinoctiall vnto either of the Poles?

Philo.   It is, as in like maner the Longitude, from the
Weſt to th' Eaſt.   Spoud.   Yet Glarianus accõp-
teth the Latitude from the North to the South, & not
from th' Equator towarde eithcr of the Poles.

Philon.   It is à ſmall errour, & you your ſelfe are able
to refute it. But nowe will I ſhewe vnto you howe muche
the circuite of th' Earth is, & then make mention of the
Zones.   Spou.   Sir, neuer take it in hande, for the
comon people will iudge you madde : ſeynge you neither
haue gone about the viij. parte of it, neither yet for want
of yeres you might acheue ſuch an enterpriſe, althoughe
you had ſo long life giuen you, as Neſtor had, becauſe of
the hougie Seas, greate Riuers, & depe Lakes, beſides
Wodes, Rockes, deſerte places, & innumerable perils:
which I can not repete.   Philon.   You haue trewly
ſayd, if ther were none other way to atteine to it, thẽ by
traueling about it: but it ſhalbe ſufficient to haue traueled any portiõ of this great circuit. For Ptolomæus ſheweth how to find out the Circuit of th' Earth, by ſearching
the diſtaunce of à great Circle, cõprehended betwixt the
vertical points of two (or more) places, diſtaũt à ſunder.

                                          Spoud.

What Latitud
is.

Glarianus
errour.

Howe to finde
out the Circuit
of th' Earth.

*The verticall
Poynte, Zenit
or Pole of the
Horizont, is so
much distante
from the E-
quinoctiall,
how much the
Pole is eleua-
ted aboue the
Horizõt. And
like as the me-
ridian, euer do
describe the
Northe and
Southe costes:
so dothe the
verticall Pa-
rallele, the
East and
West.

Spoud. By what meane shall I finde out the vertical
point*? Phi. It is equall to the Pole Arctike (the finding
of whiche, hereafter I will teache you) & you maye vse
th'one for th'other: thẽ you also in like maner must know
the distaunce in miles of these places, after diuid the distaunce of the two places, by the differẽce of the two verticall pointes, & the quotiẽt shall shew you howe manye
miles do answere to one degree of the saide Circle in the
Heaũes. But or we further proced, marke this figure, in
which C. is th'earth, A.B.
the distaunce of two placis
in th'Earth, D. E. the
space of the greate Circle
in Heauen, betwixte the
two verticall pointes.

Now diuiding the space,
A.B. by D.E. the quotiẽt
shal shew the nũber of mi
les. As for exãple: I take th'eleuatiõ of the pole at Portſmouth, whiche is the furdest place on the south shore of
Englande, & finde it, 51. degr. 20. minutes: & in like
sort at Barwike, the furdest place North, whose Latitud is 56. deg. 50. mi. The differẽce of these. 2. eleuatiõs
is 5. degrees, 30. minutes. Also the directe distaũce from
Portſmouth to Barwicke, is 330. miles. Therefore diuiding the. 330. miles (which is the portiõ of th'Earth, answering the differẽce of these 2. Eleuatiõs) by the 5. degrees, & 30. minutes, which is the difference: I find the
quotient

An example.

quotient to be.60.Wherefore in all places in Englande 60.miles, anſwer to one degre of any great Circle in the heauen. Spoud. Then J pray you retorne to your figure againe, and conferre it with your example.

Philo. J wil ſo do. Firſt. A. do repreſent Barwike. B in like maner Portſmouth, whoſe eleuations of the pole Arcticke is ſet ouer their heades. The diſtance frō. A. to. B. 330. miles, the portion of the heauen betwixte the ij. eleuations is. 5. degrees. 30. minuts: by which I did deuide the diſtance of th'Earth. A. B. findinge the quotient. 60. And in like ſorte you may worke with anye other places in th'Earth.

Spoud. This ſerueth well for to knowe what portion of th'Earthe in Englande, anſwereth to th'Arke of anye greate Circle conteined betwixt the Zenit of two ſeuerall places. But what is thys in reſpect of the Circuit & compaſſe of the hole Earth?

Philo. Yet by this you are able to declare how manye miles anſwer to. 30. degrees?

Spou. Yea verely, and that eaſely. Philo. And by the ſame ordre you may find that. 21600. Engliſh miles, anſwere vnto. 360. degrees whyche is the compaſſe of the heauēs. Spou. This is ſo euident that all men muſt nedes cōfeſſe it, but it ſemeth very meruailus. Ph. What ſay you then (which is more) if J make you preſentlye to find how many barly cornes in thicknes wil go about the Horizont, if thei might be placed equally? Spo. It ſemeth impoſſible to be brought to paſſe by any mans deuiſe, & therfore you had beſt omit the worke.

G.i.   Philo.

Phi. You know how many barly cornes will extend the legth of an English mile? *Spo.* Yes sir, you said .25344o. maketh a mile in length. *Phi.*   Thē if .25344o. cornes make a mile: shall not 5474304000. barly cornes answer to .21600 miles? *Spo.* And is there any difference towchīg the cōpasse of th'earth? *Ph.* Yes for Ptolo. saith 22500. mil. the circuit of th'earth. *Tibitius & Alphraganus* but .20400. *Eratosthenes* .31250. & *Hipparchus* 34625. *Spo.* And you differ frō thē all: but wherof doth all this diuersitie spring? *Phi.*   Ether of the diuersitie of the measures, or els that the places Latitudes wer' not exactly knowē. As *Ptolom.* making example of *Alexādria & Rodia*, calleth *Rodia* 36. deg. & 50. mi: Wher it is 38 degr. & .30. min. now behold the Figure.

Diuersitie of opinions touching th'earth his circuit.

And seyng you haue learned sufficiently what the Lõgitude, Latitude, Circuit, or Compasse of th'Earth is : it should seme very requisite to make playne relatiõ, which places of th'Earth are habitable, & which be not.

Spoud.   That thing is very expedient aswel, for the conseruation, as also reperation, & restoring a man vnto health lost. For by that inuention the temperature of th'Aëre, is easely founde out.

Phil.   You haue well spoken, & therfore we wyll conuerte our talke vnto the zones.

Spou.   It should seme first requisite to declare the nature of Paralleles, for by the distinction of them (as I remēber) the Zones are founde out.   Philo. It is so, but here note that there are Paralleles which diuideth the Longitude of Regions, & are called Paralleles of Longitude, & also Paralleles of Climates (which in there place I will declare) makinge here mention but of v.onely, which haue principall vse in the distinctiõ of zones. As th'equinoctial, the ij. tropikes, the circles Arctike, & Antarctike. And these deuide the face of th'Earth in fiue portiõs, or partes, & are called zones, in French bēdes, & we may aptly call thē equidistaunt places, or Girdles.   Spou.   And howe is th'Earth diuided into fiue Zones according to the v. parallele Circles? Phi. I will shewe you after Parmenides mind, vnto whõ Possidonius (as Strabo witnesseth) ascribeth th'inuentiõ. First directly vnder th'equinoctial in the heauēs, ther is also in the mides of th'earth an Equino.imagined, & vnder the tropick in the heauē,

. What a Zone is.

Parmenides.
Possidomus.

G.ij.   two

two tropike Circles in th'Earth : and finallye, vnder the two polary circles in the Heauen, two circles in th'Earth answering in like proportiõ: so that th'Earth is parted in v.equall portiõs, which are called zones, as this Figure doeth manifestly set out.

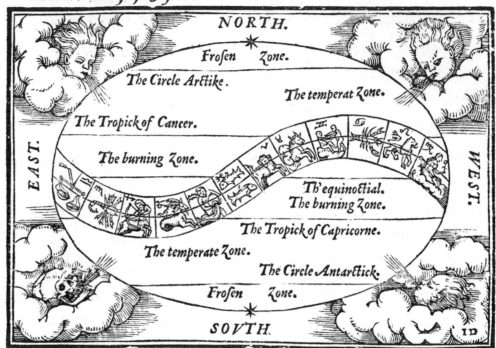

Spoud. *Do you not in this Figure call euery portion betwixt two paralleles: à zone?* Phil. *Yes verely, as the space betwixt the tropike of Cãcer, & Capricorn, in Græke is called* Διαχεχαυμдώη, *with vs the burning zone, because the sonne goeth ouer th'inhabitauntes heades cõtinually. Also betwixt the tropicke of Cancer, & the Circle Arctike,* Εὔχρατος. *or the temperate zone. And the portiõ betwixt the circle Arctick & the north Pole* Βόρειος *we call it Frosen. In lyke maner with th'other two zones southe from th'Equinoctiall, the temperate south zone is called* Αὐτεύχρατος, *and the frosen zone,* Νότιος.

Spou.

The bur-
ning zone.

Temperate
zones.

Frosē Zones

Spou. *Yet by my computation your table sheweth sexe zones: Two frosen zones, two temperate, and two burninge zones: for the space betwixte the two Tropicke Paralleles, is deuided equally of th'Equinoctiall.*

Phi. *You are in the same error that Polybius was (as testifieth Strabo) but Proclus hereto do aptly answer, where he speke of zones, and I will repeate his wordes of this burning zone only, omitting the rest, whereby it shalbe euident vnto you, that there are not two, but one burning zone, his wordes are these.*

Polybius error.

Περὶ τῶν πέντε ζωνῶν.

Η δὲ λοιπὴ, μέση τ̄ προειρημένων, κειμένη δὲ ἐπ' αὐτὴν τὴν τοῦ ἡλίου πάροδον, διακεκαυμένη χαλεῖται· διχοτομεῖται δι' αὐτὴ ὑπὸ τοῦ ἐν τῇ γῇ ἰσημερινοῦ κύκλου.

Reliqua quę inter memoratas quatuor medium locū tenet, quod sub ipso Solis transitu iacet, torrida nuncupatur: à terestri equatore in duas partes diuisa.

Th'other zone (saith Proclus) which is in the mids of the .iiij. aforesaid, because it lieth vnder the course of the sonne, is called burning: and is deuided of th'earthly Æquinoctiall, in two equall portions. Spoud. *But what compelled Proclus to saye that it is but one zone: Seinge it is deuided in two, by the aforesaide earthlye Æquinoctiall? I wil tel you, because ther is no alteratiō of the quality, & tēperature of the heauēs betwixt the space and distance of the .ij. Tropikes, but continuallye hote al the yere (by resō of the sōnes iornay in the zodiake as in the figure you may se) therfore not only Proclus but also Plato, Aristotle, Strabo, Ouide ād Virgil yea & al authors do make their accōpt but of .v. zones.* Spo. *It shuld seme that this burning zone, for the feruēt heat, & the .ij. frosen zones so far distant from the sōnes course, shuld not be habitable, as Ouide doth right excellently in these verses set out.*

An obiection.

Lib.1.Metamorphos.

G.iij.

Vtq; duæ dextra cœlum, totidemq; siniftra
Parte, secant zonæ: quinta eft ardentior illis:
Sic onus inclufum numero diftinxit eodem
Cura dei, totidemq; plagæ tellere præmuntur:
Quarum, quæ media eft, non eft habitabilis æftu.
Nix tegit alta duas, totidem inter vtrafq; locauit,
Temperiemque dedit, mifta cum frigore flamma.

Like as the Zones into v. partes do right the Heauens diuide,
Euen so, for th'Earth à nûbre like, nature did well prouide
The middeft of thē all men efchew, the burning is so fell.   (dwell.
In the zones next the Poles through could, no creature long maye
Bitwixt thefe, & the burning Zone, two other fe you may,
For tempratnes repleniſhed with liuinge thinges alway.

The Anfwer.   Philo.   Well, bycauſe J will not haue you to erre with
Poëtes, & other that fuppofe thefe not habitable, I will
take the more diligence to driue this Herefie out of your
Ptolomæus.   heade, & althoughe Ptolomæus, & Auicenna were of
Auicenna.   fufficient authoritie, to make you credit this thing, affir-
minge that they haue fene men whiche did inhabite be-
twixt th'Equinoctiall, & the tropike of Cancer: yea, &
that, ther ar many notable Cities, & Villages: yet J wil
vfe other reafons then teftimonies in this behalfe. And
firft anfwer me: Is not the heate of the Sōne cauſe (that
in the Sūmer ceafon he inclining toward our habitatiō)
that mens colour in ther faces & hādes are made blacker, then naturally they are?

Spoud.   Yes verely: & J haue fene fome dwellers in
litle Vilages, as Plowmen, Heardmen, & Shepehards
marueloufly fonneburnt.   Philon.   What wil you
cōiecture then of thofe people that are blacke, face, body
& all externe partes of them, doeth it not come of the
heate of the Sōne?   Spoud.   It mufte nedes fo be,
and J haue fene men of that colour, & we call them
Æthi-

Æthiopians.   Philo. *Very well, & do not you beleue that the countrey where they dwell, must of force be
vnder the beames of the Sõne?   Spou. Els it could
not folow that ther colour should so much differ frõ ours.
Philon.   And there is no place vnder the perpendi-
culer Sõne beames, but only this burning Zone: & Ara
bia (sumwhat frõ the Sõne beames situated) is the cause
that th'inhabitauntes, are not so blacke as the Æthiopians: nor the Spaniardes, as th'Arabians: or Frẽchmẽ,
as the Spaniardes.   Spoud.   And the Germaynes
haue their skinne whiter then the Frenchemen : & we
here in Englande, then all these: so that the furder from
this burninge Zone, the whiter the skie : and the nerer
th'Equinoctiall, the blacker, & more adust & burnt.
Philo.   Moreouer the Nauigatiõ to Calicute, (of
which voiage Vesputius, & Columbus were the first au-* Vesputius
thors, & nowe more frequented of the spanierdes, then   Columbus.
sayling into coũtreis nie adiacẽt to vs) do witnes beare,
that vnder this burning Zone there are inhabitaũtes.
Spou. by these wordes it is manifest, that the burning
Zone is not habitable onely, but also inhabited. And as
touchinge the temperate Zones, no man is so folishe, or
madde, as to denie them to be replenished with all liuing
creatures abũdantly: wherfore if you can proue that the
two Zones, next the Poles are also habitable, you shall
as farre banish this errour frõ me, as the Sõne doth dar-
kenes.   Philoni.   Although Ptolomæus do not
describe any parallele beyonde Thylim, whiche is two
degr. & more of this side of the Circle Arctike.   And*

G.iiij.   that

that for the situatiõ of it, farre distant from the beames
of the sonne, and therfore the Waters cõtinually frosen
and th'Earth with Snow couered: Yet Erasmus Reignholt (and that truley) describeth a Parallele by Hiel-
so, an Ilãd in Norway which is. 9. degrees beyonde the
polary or Arctike circle. Also the grene lande, and in diuers countreis there inhabited, and the inhabitants are
called in Greke περίσκιοι in Latine Periscij, and we may
call them aptly inhabitantes which haue there shadowe
daily declininge vnto all partes of the Horizont.

Spo.　Then I perceiue that both the burning zone, &
also the frosen are habitable and not that only , but also
inhabited, although not so plentifullye as the temperate
zone. But nowe sence ther is offered good occasion to intreat of shadowes, and their diuersitie, yea and the place
serueth aptly for it, or we do further procede. Wherfore
I require you, to turne our cõmunicatiõ to this matter.

Phi.　With a right willing mind. You must first vnderstãd that of the diuersitie of shadowes, ther ar .iij. diuers
distinct habitatiõs of people found, that is to say, Α'μφίσκιοι,
Ε'τερόσκιοι, Περίσκιοι. whiche names also the latinest vse, Amphiscij, Heteroscij, Periscij, & we wãt apt English ter-
mes for them, yet I will make it plain thoughe I vse the
more wordes. And first I wil speke of those which we call
Amphiscij. You do marke wel that the sonnes course, &
recourse continuallie in the Zodiak maketh the shadow
long, and short? Spou.　I know that well, and the nerer he cometh toward vs , the shorter is the shadow, and
the furder he goeth frõ vs, the lõger he geueth a shadow.
　　　　　　　　　　　　　　　　　　Philo.

Erasmus
Reignholt.

Amphiscij.

Philo. *It is fo as you fay.But how thinke you, is ther not fome place that hath no fhadow?* Spoud. *There can be no fuch.* Philo. *If the greateft declination of the Sonne from th'Equinoctiall nere to the zenit,& ver ticall poynt,make the fhadow fhorteft that can be in thy region:then where he goeth ouer any zenit,there mufte be no fhadow.* Spou. *It fhould feme to follow.* Phil. *Yea it mufte of neceffitie fo be.* Spoud. *But where is there any fuch, ouer whofe heades the Sŏne di- rectly goeth?* Philo. *Suche be thofe that dwell in the burning Zone,which(as I faid)is betwixt the two Tropikes,fo that when the Sonne is in the beginning of Aries,and Libra,they haue no fhadowe, and therefore Plinius calleth thē* Ασκιοὶ, *Afcij, or people withoute fha-* *dow.And becaufe he is twife yerely in thefe poynts,thei haue two fommers,and in like cafe two winters,for that he declineth to the Tropikes of Cancer,and Capricorne. Wherfore Lucanus fpake of fuch inhabitants very apt- ly, in this thefe verfes following.*

Afcij hath two Somers & two Win- ters.lib.9.

Libro.9.

  Deprænfum eft hunc effelocum,quo circulusalti
   Zolftitii,medium fignorum percutit orbem.
  This is the place where th'Equinoctiall diuides
   The Zodiake in twaine,caufinge two Somer tides.

Spoud. *I remember that Ptolomæus in his Alme- gift maketh mention of fuch inhabitantes, and nameth alfo fuch as dwel vnder the tropikes Afcij,but yet I fhuld not haue called it to mind if you had not geuē th'occatiō.* Philo. *Yet thys people whan as the fonne declyneth Northward from them,haue a fhadow,which fhadow falleth at none ftede directlye fouthe(for of other fha-*

Lib.2.cap.4.

            dowes

dowes I make no accompte). Spoud. *It must neades
so be, for the sone is North frō that thing which geueth
the shadowe.* Philon. *And whan the sonne is in the
winter poynt, vnto what coste do the shadowe decline?*
Spoud. *It shall fall directly North by the reason of
you aleaged.* Philo. *Here then you se the cause wher
of these inhabitauntes were called Amphiscij, and we
maye call them double or two folde shadowed.*

Heteroscij. Spou. *I vnderstand your meaning.* Philon. *The
second be those, which haue the shadow continuallye, toward one coste, ether North or South.* Spou. *Then
we be in the numbre of those, for we haue oure shadow
directly North.*

Antipodes. Phi. *And such be those that dwel in th'opposite place of
th'earth against vs (& therfore called Antipodes. For
the sonne neuer comminge ouer their zenit, they haue
the shadow into the South coste perpetually declining, as
we haue into the Northe.* Spou. *This muste nedes
be certainly true, but yet I do much meruaile therat.*
Phil. *What so euer is rare, and not commonly sene and
hard, is euer meruelous. And the Arabians commynge
into Europe, meruailed as muche to see the shadowe
Northwarde, as you do to here it is declined (with the
aforesaid inhabitants) toward the South cost, & ther-
Lib.3.   fore Lucanus speaketh of them in this sort.*

Ignotum vobis (Arabes) venistis in orbem,
Vmbras mirati nemorum non iri sinistras.
A Region vnknowne (Arabians) you finde:
Musing that the shadow, is still North declinde.

Spou.

Spou. *There remaineth yet to speke of the thirde sort of people which you named Periscij.* Phil. *They toke* Perifcij. *that name because thei(dwelling within the circles arc tike & Antarctike) haue the shadow going round about the Horizont.* Spou. *But yet the shadowe moueth not so swiftlye aboute th'Earth with them, as it doeth with vs (and those you call Amphiscios) for wyth vs it goeth about from the West by the Northe, & so to the East in the space(that the sonne is in oure Hemisphere, & aboue th'earth,whiche at the most is in.xvij. houres.* Phi. *It is so.* Spou. *Thē seing the sonne goeth not out of ther sight for the space of.182.dais, & xij. hours, whiche is there continuall daye:then it should go aboute the horizont but in that lōg place.* Phi. *That is false.* fpace *For how think you,doth not the sonne circuit th'earth in xxiiij.houres continuallye?* Spou. *Yes verely.* Phil. *Thē doth the shadow go about their Horizōt in the same space of time,except you imagin those Perisci-os,to dwel without the circuit of th'earth.* Spo. *That were a poynt of demency or madnes:so that as oftē as he circuith th'earth,so oftē in lik case do ther shadow turne about the place of their horizont,which must neades be 182.times.* Phi. *I am glad you vnderstand the reasō of it, and now behold the table of shadowes.*

A TABLE, OF SHADOVVES, SHEVVING
THEIR PROPORTION VNTO THE GNOMON
(it beyng deuided in 60.partes)for euery degree of the Sonnes altitude:
and also the quantie of the Shadow in euery Country,Region,
& City,thorowe the vniuerfall Earthe,
whan the Sonne is in the Æqui-
noctiall,and Solsticiall
poyntes.

The Sonnes Altitude	The Shadow		Th'elevatio of the Pole	Shadow solstitial in somer		Æquinoctiall Shadow		Shadow Solsticiall in wi.	
	par.	Mi		par.	Mi	par.	Mi	par.	Mi
1	3437	24	1	24	49	1	3	27	18
2	1718	10	2	23	36	2	5	28	35
3	1144	52	3	22	24	3	8	29	53
4	858	2	4	21	13	4	11	31	12
5	685	48	5	20	3	5	15	32	32
6	570	51	6	18	53	6	18	33	54
7	488	39	7	17	44	7	22	35	18
8	426	55	8	16	36	8	26	36	44
9	378	49	9	15	29	9	30	38	11
10	340	16	10	14	22	10	34	39	40
11	308	40	11	13	16	11	39	41	12
12	282	16	12	12	10	12	45	42	45
13	259	53	13	11	5	13	51	44	21
14	240	38	14	10	0	14	57	46	0
15	223	55	15	8	56	16	4	47	41
16	209	14	16	7	52	17	12	49	24
17	196	15	17	6	48	18	20	51	11
18	184	39	18	5	45	19	29	53	2
19	174	15	19	4	42	20	39	54	56
20	164	50	20	3	38	21	50	56	53
21	156	18	21	2	35	23	2	58	54
22	148	30	22	1	32	24	14	61	0
23	141	21	23	0	29	25	28	63	10
24	134	45	24	0	33	26	43	65	25
25	128	39	25	1	36	27	58	67	45
26	123	0	26	2	38	29	15	70	11
27	117	45	27	3	41	30	34	72	43
28	112	50	28	4	44	31	54	75	21
29	108	14	29	5	48	33	15	78	7
30	103	54	30	6	52	34	38	81	0
31	99	51	31	7	56	36	3	84	2
32	96	1	32	9	0	37	20	87	13
33	92	23	33	10	4	38	57	90	34
34	88	57	34	11	8	40	28	94	5
35	85	41	35	12	14	42	1	97	49
36	82	34	36	13	19	43	35	101	45
37	79	37	37	14	25	45	12	105	56
38	76	48	38	15	32	46	52	110	23
39	74	5	39	16	40	48	35	115	8
40	71	30	40	17	48	50	20	120	11
41	69	1	41	18	57	52	9	125	39
42	66	38	42	20	6	54	1	131	30
43	64	28	43	21	16	55	57	137	49
44	62	8	44	22	27	57	56	144	40
45	60	0	45	23	39	60	0	152	7
46	57	56	46	24	53	62	8	160	16
47	55	57	47	26	7	64	20	169	12
48	54	1	48	27	22	66	38	179	4
49	52	9	49	28	39	69	1	190	0
50	50	20	50	29	56	71	30	202	14
51	48	35	51	31	15	74	5	216	0
52	46	52	52	32	37	76	48	231	35
53	45	12	53	33	59	79	37	249	26
54	43	35	54	35	23	82	34	270	5
55	42	1	55	36	48	85	41	294	15
56	40	28	56	38	15	88	57	322	57
57	38	57	57	39	45	92	23	357	35
58	37	29	58	41	16	96	1	400	16
59	36	3	59	42	50	99	51	454	12
60	34	38	60	44	26	103	54	524	34
61	33	15	61	46	5	108	14	620	17
62	31	54	62	47	46	112	50	758	8
63	30	34	63	49	30	117	45	974	1
64	29	15	64	51	17	123	0	1360	36
65	27	58	65	53	8	128	39	2253	44
66	26	43	66	55	1	134	45	6547	56
67	25	28	67	56	59	141	21	Infinite	
68	24	14	68	59	1	148	30	num,	
69	23	2	69	61	6	156	18	bre.	
70	21	50	70	63	17	164	50		
71	20	39	71	65	32	174	15		
72	19	29	72	67	52	184	39		
73	18	20	73	70	18	196	15		
74	17	12	74	72	51	209	14		
75	16	4	75	75	29	223	55		
76	14	57	76	78	15	240	38		
77	13	51	77	81	9	259	53		
78	12	45	78	84	11	282	16		
79	11	39	79	87	23	308	40		
80	10	34	80	90	44	340	16		
81	9	30	81	94	16	378	49		
82	8	26	82	98	0	426	55		
83	7	22	83	101	58	488	39		
84	6	18	84	106	9	570	51		
85	5	15	85	110	37	685	48		
86	4	11	86	115	23	858	2		
87	3	8	87	120	28	1144	52		
88	2	5	88	125	56	1718	10		
89	1	3	89	131	48	3437	24		
90	0	0	90	138	9	Infinite			

Ther may many cōclusions by this table be wrought as
you shal know or we depart: but now let vs furder proced
cōcerninge our talke of zones, in which you must cōsider
that these zones of which we haue intreated, ar deuided
into climates, & regions. Spo. How doth à climat and
à zone differ, they both wer for this cause first inuented,
to make diuision of the face of th'earth into sōdry parts.
Philo. If confesse no lesse, but they differ in this poynt, *How a Zone*
that à Zone doth in it cōtain the fift portiō of th'earth, *& a Climate*
and à climate but only so much of th'earth, & the lōgest *differ.*
day in that place, do differ from th'equinoctial. xxx. mi-   as
nutes, or half an hour, and are named. vii. in numbre, of
all th'auncient Geographers.
Spoud. Then the first climate shalbe in latitude. xvi.
degrees. xliiij. minutes from th'equinoctiall, and the lōgest day, shall excede. xij. houres (whiche is the quantitie of the daye vnder th'equinoctiall) one houre: for so
saithe Ptolomæus.

Philon. It is true, but heare you muste consider, that *Ptolomæus de-*
Ptolomæus deuideth euery climate in. iiij. equall porti- *uision of Cli-*
ons, & nameth them Paralleles: euery one of them cō- *mates.*
teining in latitude. iiij. degrees, xviij. min. incresing the
quantity of the longest day. xv. minutes: so that Ptolomæus (making the first climate xvi. degrees, xliiij. min.
in Latitude from th'equinoctiall) meaneth the middes,
and not the beginning of the climate. Spou. If praye
you or we anye further proceade shewe me the signification of a Parallele. Philo. Παράλληλος *in Greke* (whiche *What a Pa-*
we also do call à Parallele) is à Circle equally distaunt, *rallele is.*

                    Hj.   from

from that which is drawne next him, and are deſcribed
by the courſe of the ſonne and ſtarres, of which the greateſt is th'equinoctial: for that he is furdeſt frō the Poles,
ſo that the nerer the poles, the leſſe is the parallele: and
the number of them Ptolomæus maketh .xxj. as in this
figure, in which I haue made .xxj. paralleles frō th'equi-

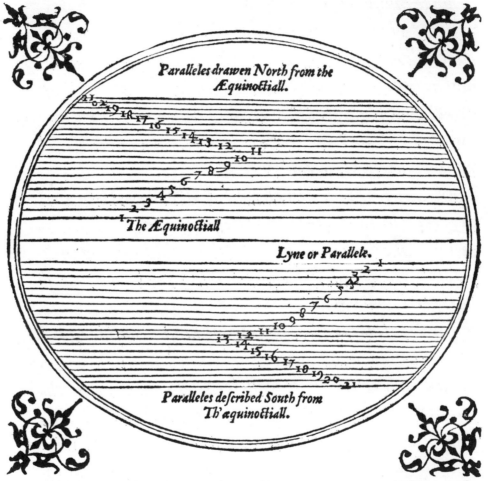

noctiall, vnto both the poles Arctike & Antarctike, and
now to our matter againe from whence we did digreſſe.
You ſhall conſider that euerye Climate hathe à proper
name, for the ſuerer difference of one from an other:
and

& taketh his name of some notable Citye, Mountaine, or Riuer, ouer which the mids of that Climate is drawn As for example.

The middes of the firste Climate goeth ouer a notable Flande of Nilus, called Meroë & of that we name it Dia Meroes, that is, the climat going ouer Meroë.

The seconde Climat is called Dia Syënes of à citye in Egipt called Syënes.

The middes of the thirde climate is drawen ouer Alexandria, an other Citye also in Egipt & therfore called Dialexandrias.

The fourth goth ouer th'Fland of the Rodes, now in subiection to the great Turke, and is named Diarhodou.

The fift climate Dia Romes going ouer Rome somtime the head of the world, at this preset the sinck of sin.

The sixte Climate is named Dia Pontou, because it goeth ouer the Pontike seas named Euxinus.

The seuenth is drawe by Boristhenes a Citye so called & therefore named Diaboristheneos, & not by the Riphean Mountanes as the vnlerned sort suppose: seing that they ar at the lest. x. deg. frō this climate distaunte. Spou. And what was the cause that they described no places, beyōd the. 7. climate: seing that ther are many inhabitāts, (as by your words do appeare) wher you made mention of the habitable places in th'earth?

Philo. Jt was, ether because they supposed those places scāt, or with muche paines habitable for th'extreme cold: or els, that they knew not the parts North frō thē situated, as now we do, Spou. And do they not make

mention of Climates drawne South from th'equinoctiall
as of the North, of whiche you haue spoken?

Phi.   They do in like maner deuide that portion, into

vij.Climates: but for that they knewe no notable places,
(as in the north partes from th'equinoctiall)they gaue
them the names of the North Climates, with this addi-
tion Anti (that is to saye oppositie or againste) as An-
tidiameroes, the Climate Southe from th'equinoctiall,
opposite or agaynst the north Climat, drawn by Meroë.
And so in like sort with th'other, as this figure shewith, in

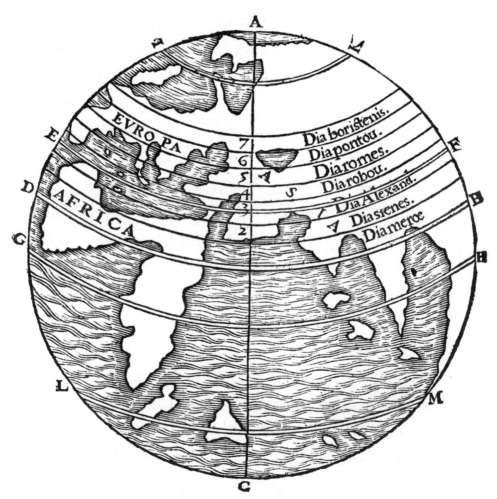

which

which.A.B.C.D.do reprefente the meridian circle, A.
the Northe Pole, and.C.the Pole Antarctike.B.D.
th'equinoctiall.E.F.the Tropike of Cancer:G.H.the
Tropike of Capricorne:the Polary circles.I.K.and.L.
M. The Climates of them felfes are euident, hauinge
their proper names, to them ioyned:& are drawn from
B.D.th'equinoctiall, toward the poles.A.C.

Spou. Now I pray you declare the cotinuation of the
Climates,& paralleles. Philo. J wil fulfill your re-
queft. The partes of th'Earth Northwardes beinge by
painfull,& dagerous nauigatios found out, are deuided
alfo into Climates, we folowing the fame ordre that Pto
lomæus, and th'aunciente Geographers vfed:that is, e-
uery parallele to be diftaunt from an other.4.degrees,
18.minutes:and euery climate one from an other 7.de-
grees 27.minutes:geuing them in like fort apte names
of the places ouer which they are drawne:fo that in our
time, there is founde after the fame inuention 96.Pa-
ralleles, of which are made 24.climates, and for that it
fhall not eafely be breuied in the poke of Obliuio, behold
I haue drawne out a Table, conteining in it the paralleles & Climates with the places ouer which they directli
are defcribed : as alfo th'eleuation of the pole Arctike,
vnto 90.degrees:and the quantity of the longeft daye,
anfweringe vnto euery one of thofe degrees, whiche
Table fhall muche pleafure you, as hereafter it fhall be euident.

The quantitie of climates & Paralleles.

Hiij.   A Table con-

Paralleles after Ptolomæus.	Paralleles movecertayn & exacte.	The number of Climates after th'olde Grecians vse.	Climates after th'inuention of Geographers in our time.	The names of Climates & Paralleles after som notable place in them.	Th'Eleuation of the Pole articck.		The quantitie of the longest day.	
1	1		1	Vnder Th'Equinoctuall.	0	0	12	0
2	2				4	18	12	15
3	3		2		8	34	12	30
4	4				12	43	12	45
5	5	1	3	By th'Ilande Meroë.	16	44	13	0
6	6				20	34	13	15
7	7	2	4	By Syëne vnder the Tropicke of Cancer.	24	11	13	30
8	8				27	36	13	45
9	9	3	5	By Alexandria.	30	48	14	0
10	10				33	46	14	15
11	11	4	6	By the Rhodes.	36	30	14	30
12	12				39	3	14	45
13	13	5	7	By Rome.	41	23	15	0
14	14				43	32	15	15
15	15	6	8	By Ponte Euxine.	45	31	15	30
16	16				47	21	15	45
17	17	7	9	By Boreithenes.	49	1	16	0
18	18				50	34	16	15
19	19		10	By VViteberge.	51	59	16	30
20	20				53	17	16	45
21	21		11	By Grypsualde.	54	30	17	0
22	22				55	36	17	15
23	23		12	By Moscouia & Irlande.	56	38	17	30
24	24				57	34	17	45
25	25		13		58	27	18	0
	26				59	15	18	15
26	27		14		59	59	18	30
	28				60	40	18	45
27	29		15		61	8	19	0
	30				61	53	19	15
28	31		16	By Orcades.	62	25	19	30
	32				62	55	19	45
29	33		17		63	22	20	0
	34				63	47	20	15
	35		18		64	10	20	30
	36				64	31	20	45
30	37		19	All these Paralleles folowynge are drawen by places in Norwey, and Sweuelãd &c.	64	49	21	0
	38				65	6	21	15
	39		20		65	22	21	30
	40				65	35	21	45
31	41		21		65	47	22	0
	42				65	58	22	15
	43		22		66	7	22	30
	44				66	15	22	45
32	45		23		66	21	23	0
	46				66	25	23	15
	47		24		66	29	23	30
	48			Vnder th'Arct. Circle.	66	31	23	43
33	49				66	32	24	0

Paralleles after Ptolomæus.	Paralleles more certaine and exacte.	The names of the Paralleles after the notable places, by which they are deſcribed.&c.	Th'Eleuation of the Pole Artik.		Continuall day in ſommer.		Continuall nyght in winter.	
	50		67	0	23	11	22	1
34	51		67	30	33	17	31	13
	52		68	0	41	14	39	2
	53		68	30	48	6	45	8
	54		69	0	54	3	50	22
	55		79	30	59	12	56	0
35	56		70	0	64	11	60	16
	57		70	30	69	4	65	2
	58		71	0	73	13	69	6
	59		71	30	77	17	73	5
	60	Bp Laponia and the grene Lande	72	0	81	17	77	1
	61		72	30	85	14	80	17
	62	whiche after the opiniō of ſundry	73	0	89	8	84	6
36	63	Authors do continually without	73	30	92	22	87	18
	64	ſeperation Ioine with weſt India.	74	0	96	10	91	2
	65		74	30	99	21	94	9
	66		75	0	103	5	97	14
	67		75	30	106	11	100	17
	68		76	0	109	16	103	19
	69		76	30	112	20	106	20
	70		77	0	115	22	109	20
	71		77	30	118	22	118	17
	72		78	0	121	22	118	14
37	73		78	30	124	21	118	11
	74		79	0	127	19	121	7
	75		79	30	130	17	124	2
	76		80	0	133	13	126	20
	77		80	30	136	8	129	14
	87		81	0	139	3	132	7
	79		81	30	141	21	135	0
	80		82	0	144	14	137	17
	81		82	30	147	7	140	9
	82		83	0	150	0	142	23
	83		83	30	152	16	145	13
38	84		84	0	155	8	148	4
	85		84	30	158	0	150	18
	86		85	0	160	15	153	9
	87		85	30	163	5	155	22
	88		86	0	165	19	158	12
	89		86	30	168	19	161	2
	90		87	0	170	23	163	15
	91		87	30	173	13	166	4
	92		88	0	176	2	168	16
	93		88	30	178	16	171	6
	94		89	0	181	5	173	19
	95		89	30	183	19	176	9
	96		90	0	186	7	178	22

Spou. Can they not in like maner, draw paralleles from th'Æquinoctiall Southward as they do North, yea & geue them the same names of the Northe paralleles, with the Greke propoſition anti, as thei do in climates? _Phi._ Yes verely, & they ſo do, vntill by their trauels

South Paralleles.

they haue found out the Regiõs, Ilands, Hilles, Riuers & ſuch notable things, of which in like ſort the ſouth climates & paralleles may take denomination. As at this preſ̃et ther ar South paralleles, which are oppoſite to the North, & places foũd out, of which they may veri aptly take name.

As the parallele (oppoſite vnto the North parallele, which goeth by the Canarian Ilands, is drawne by the Riuer Nilus, and Mons Lunæ, the Mount of the Moone.

The parallele oppoſite to that which is drawne by Syëne, goeth by the Ilandes Mendacaſcar, Peuta, Necura, the greater Iaua, Candin, and the kingdome of Coilum.

The parallele oppoſite to that whiche is drawne by Damaſcus, goth by the promontory of good hope, called promontorium bonæ Spej.

The oppoſite parallele, to that goeth ouer the Rhodes, is deſcribed by th'Ilands Seilan, & Augama.

Antipodes.

& they are antipodes vnto Italy, which dwell in Iaua the leſſer. The antipodes to the Lucitanians, are thoſe in the Iſle of Seila. There be alſo diuers other places towarde the ſouth coaſt, of which neither I haue heard of any credible perſon, nor yet red: & therfore can not affirme

firme any certeine trueth: & will omit it vntill an other
ceason.

Spou.   Yet or we procede further, J muʃt trouble
you with one doubt: & that is gathered of the Arabian
Phiʃician Auicenna, who ʃaieth, that th'Aëre is of beʃt *Auicenne.*
temperature vnder th'equinoctiall, & they are more fre
from inʃirmities of the body then we are, whome you affirme to dwell in the North temperate zone. For if the
paralleles be of this nature, that howe muche the nearer
we are th'equinoctiall, ʃo muche the greater is the heate:
and howe muche the furder remoued from th'equinoctiall, ʃo muche the colder the qualitie of the aire is : there
muʃt ʃeme à manifeʃt repugnancie, betwixt Auicenne,
& the Geographers.

Philo.   J will anʃwer you. Auicenna meaneth not that *Auicenna de-*
the temperature of th'Aëre is in à meane, neither vehe- *fended.*
ment hote, nor yet extreame could vnder th'Equinoctial,
for that were an euident errour, but becauʃe the Sonne
declineth not more then .23. digrees. 28. minutes frō the
verticall pointe, therfore ther can be no cōtrary qualitie
ingendred: as horible could, ʃo that th'Aëre is not ʃubiect
tu alteration, & contrary qualities, as oures is . & that
is the cauʃe why Auicenna thought t moʃt temperat, & *Aphoriʃ.3.*
hereto agreeth Hippocrates :   i   *propoʃi.1*

Ἀι μεταϐολαὶ τῶν ὡρέων μάλιστα τίκτȣσι νοσήματα: κὴ ἐν τῆσιν ὥρῃσιν ἀι μεγάλαι με-
ταλλαγαὶ ἤ ψύξιος, ἤ θάλψιος, κὴ τ' ἄλλα κατὰ λόγον ȣτως.

    Mutationes temporum maximè pariunt morbos, & in ipʃis tem-
poribus magnæ mutationes aut frigoris, aut æʃtus, aliaq; congruenter
ratione eodemmodo.

                                     that is

that is.The mutation of times do chefely ingender sicknesse:and in the same times,great chaunge either of heate or colde,or other qualities in like sorte.

Then seyng there is no mutation of qualitie of th'Aëre, it is thought temperat. And for that this place is iudged most temperate, there be some that suppose Can Eden, that is to say,Paradise,to be situated vnder th'Equinoctiall, as a place of pleasure, voluptiousnes, voide of Alteration, & cōtrary qualities:Yea, & Lira, interpreting Genesis, (where Moses speaketh that Adam,being expulsed from this place of pleasure & ioye, for breakyng the cōmaundement: Cherubyn kepte it with a sirie sword)saith that the fiery sword is no other thinge then the burning zone.And Polybius with Eratosthenes(as Strabo witnesse)doth affirme the temperatest dwelling to be vnder th'equinoctiall. Spoud. Seinge you haue made mention of the place most excellent of other in the Earth for pleasure.I pray you let me heare your minde concerning Hell the place of all other most horrible,& painfull,as bothe Christians and Ethinckes do confesse. Phil. I will not much of that thing speke, but if Hell be in that place whiche is furdest from the heauen, as paine & grief is furdest from pleasure, and ioye:then it must nedes be in the center of th'Earih,whiche is to saye that part that is in the mids of the same, for that is of all other parts furdest from the heauen.Whych is the cause that not onlye we,but also the Poëts in their tragedies, introduce persons comming out from vnder th'earth & call that place Hell, amonge other,Senica introduceth

Thyestes,

Pardaise where.

Lira.

Eratosthenes. Polybius.

Hell where.

Thyestes, coming out of hell, in this maner speking.

Opaca linquens Ditis inferni loca,
Adsum, profundo Tartari emissus Specu.

Leuing the darke places, of infernall Pluto,
Sent out from Hell pitte depe, here am I præsent lo.&c.

In Agamem-
none.

But we will leaue such curious questions, and spend the day (which so fast consumeth) in more necessary talke: for behold by my Astrolabe the sonne (being in the xxj. of Gemini) is eleuated.54.degrees, aboue the Horizōt with vs here in this plaine, and therfore he will shortlye approch to the meridian line. Spoud. Then I muste earnestly require you, to teach me some way how I may find him beinge in this line, as also other starres: for my authors make mentiō herof, affirming also that it is one of the chefe things wherwyth to find out the Longitud, and Latitude of places. Philo. I will gladly, keping nōt backe such waies as I also haue deuised to finde out th'aforsaid line. And first I wil begin with th'inuention of Glarian to find this none stede line, whiche is in thys manner. In any leuell and plaine place, with your com-passe make à circle: in what quātitye you please, in the center of whiche, you shall place a right Wyer, directlye standing vp, that it may geue a shadowe on the circle a-foresaid. Then mark the shadow which the sonne in hys rising & going down in thy Horizōt giueth, as for exā-ple. A. Is the Wier reared right vp in the center of the Circle: C. the East, & B. the West. The longest shadow that the Sonne maketh aboue the Horizont is A.D: Thē he ascending hier, makes his shadow shorter. A.E. the None steade or Meridian shadow, whiche is shor-test

To finde out
the Meridian
Line after
Glarians ma-
ner.

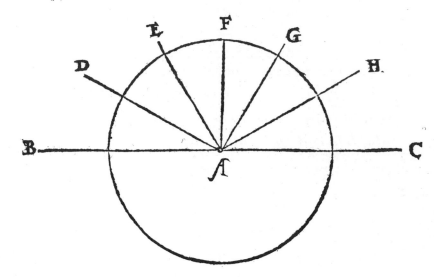

*reſt is A.F.and th'other ſhadowes G.A:H.A.are in
the like ſort the ſhadows which the ſone caſteth into the
Eaſt,after he is paſt the meridian circle,deſcending into the Weſt. Spou. Shall it be neceſſary for to obſerue
the ſhadow of the thing erected as well th'after noone,as
J do from the ſonnes riſinge vntil noone?
Philo. No verely, for whan the ſhadow doth no lenger decreſe,you drawing from the center to the circumference a ſtraight line,ſhal haue your own deſire.Other*

*The ſeconde
way.*

*willing to exchew the tediouſnes of time in obſeruation,
do prouide a Plate of Meatall, well pulliſhed, or ſome
thick planke ſmothe,and plained,in whiche is drawne a
circle as in th'other aforſaid,with a Wyer or like thynge
ſet vp right in the center,and do diligently before none
obſerue whan the ſhadow of the Wier in length is equall
with the circumference:and at th'end of it make à prick.
In like ſorte after noone whan as the ſhadowe commeth
vnto the circumference,and make there alſo à prick,thē*

with

with the compasse, deuide the space betwixte these two prickes in the middes, and make there à note or pricke: after draw à right line from the center, to that middle pricke, and it shall alwaye shewe the whan as the sonne is in the meridian or middaye line, for that eleuation of the Pole as in this example.

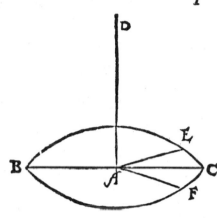

A. Is the Center B. E. C. F. the Circle drawne in the planke or plate of metall A. D. the Gnomon, or thing which geueth the shadowe, A E. the shadowe before Noone. A. F. the shadow after none: nowe deuidinge the space E. F. in the middes, whiche is .C. and drawne à righte line from A. beinge the Center, vnto C. and that is the true Meridian line.

Spoudeus. This way semeth muche easier, and facile then the other.

Philo. Yea and it is also as certaine as th'other, and it was inuented as I suppose of Iohannes de monte regio, or Vitruuius. But Vernerus vseth no other way to find The iij, waye oute thys Line, then onelye a Diall hauinge à perfaite nedle, placinge it on some plaine, and smothe place: & whan the nedle standeth stedfaftlye in the righte Line wythin the Diall, it dothe as it were poynte directlye North and South.

I.j.   Spou.

Spoud.   This waye in my iudgement doeth excell all the reſt, both for the eaſines therof & alſo (which
you can not do by th'other) that you maye by it finde the
Meridiane, or middaye Line, at all tymes bothe daye,
nyght, & houre.

Phil.   You may ſo, but the neadle doeth ſometime
erre from right north, & ſouth, as hathe bene obſerued,
& I will ſhew you in the treatiſe of Nauigation: Yea,
The iiij. way. & how you ſhall alſo correct your neadle. but I alſo haue
inuented two waies, the firſt is, I make a plaine & roũde
plate, in the mids of which I fix à ruler, hauing two ſightes to loke thorow, then whẽ the ſonne riſith halfe aboue
the Horizont, & half vnder, I (placing my Inſtrument
flat on th'earth) do direct the ruler vnto the ſame, ſo that
I may ſee him thorow the ſightes: then my ruler not moued, I drawe with à Chalke, or like thing, à right lyne frõ
the Center, vnto the Sõne, & whan the Sõne goeth down
I do in like maner drawe an other Line: then I drawe à
right Line from the Line of his riſing, vnto the Line of
his goynge downe, & diuide this Line in the middes: after I drawe a right Line from the Center, vnto the middes of the ouerwart Line, thẽ I fixe in the Center an vpright wier, the ſhadow of whiche at all times ſhall ſhewe
when as the Sonne is in the Meridiane Line in that
habitation: but or we further procede, I wyll giue you
hereof an example, in which I do make A. for the Center, then putting vpon it à wyer, or pricke, I do faſten the
ruler ther on: this beyng done, I place my inſtrumẽt flat,
& ap-

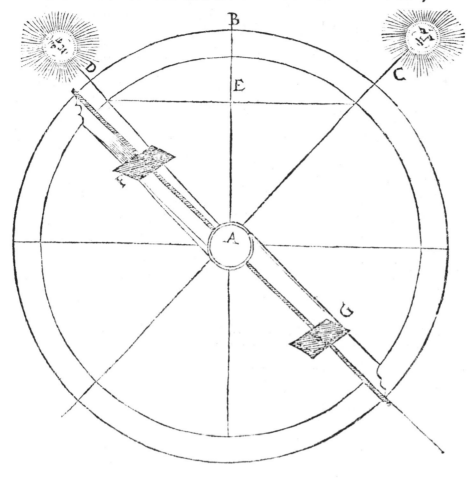

& applie the ruler with his *sightes.G.F.*vnto the S̄one,
& drawe there à Line *A.D.*in like forte, whan he is
goyng downe,*&* make an other Line *A.C.*then *I* draw
à right Line from *C.*vnto *D.*which I diuide in the middes *E.& croff*e it with à Line *A.B.*which is the Line at
midday. But in place where I cannot haue this, or other
like inftrm̄et(wh̄e as *I* fe the f̄one to draw very nere the
fouth)I pricke vpright in the groūde à knife, or fuch like
th̄ig, markīg diligētly how l̄og the fhadow doth decreafe,
& wh̄a as I perceaue it decreafeth no more, but rather

The v.way.

f.ij.   *wax*

waxe longe againe, I drawe à line from my knife, to the shadow which serueth for the Meridian line.

Spoud.   I thancke you sir, for this, your gentlenesse, in beating these things into my grose, and dulhed: And I wil put them all in practise whan conuenient time shal *To finde the* serue, but in the night (I miding to take the true height *Noonesteade* *Line by night.* of anye Planet, or fixed sterre in the nonestead lyne) what ordre shall I obserue, for then there is no shadowe, which will do pleasure. Philo.   Therfore wyth some Quadrăt, Astrolabe, or Ptolomæus ruler (the fation of whiche I do here place, and the makinge you shall finde amonge th'other Instrumentes) and marke what hys

It is made of 3. peaces, beyng 4. square: As in the Picture where A. F. is the first peace or rule. A.D. The seconde. G.D. the third rule. E. The Foote of the Staffe. C.F. The Plumrule. C.B. The ioyntes, in which the second & third Rulers are moued. K.L. The sighte holes. I. The Sonne. H. The Zenit, or verticall pointe. M. N. The Noone-Stead Lyne.

PTOLOMEVS.

altitude is, then you may staye a season: after à while obserue his hight again, and so from time, to time, vntill he increase no hier, which is a perfect token that then he is in the Meridian line. The same you maye do also with the sonne. And for that nightlye trauell hearein semeth somwhat combrous and painfull, behold here is a Table of the sonnes height, for euery degree of the signes in the Zodiake: his greatest declination being .23. degrees .28. minutes, and th'eleuation of the Pole arctike, aboue the Horizont .52. degrees, 10. minutes.

As concerning the vse of the Table, I wil speke nothing, but will reserue it for his due place, only admonishing you at this present, that first you finde out the place of the Zodiake in signes and degrees, (by some Ephemerides, or out of my tables in the Gazophilaciō Astronomicum) then loke in the ouerpart of the Table, and if that signe be there mensioned, descend downward in the first columne & finde out also the degre, and directly against it, shalt thou haue the sonnes Meridian altitude. But and the signe be found in the lower part of the Table, then you shall serch out his degre in the last column, and against it toward the left hand, you shal in like maner finde the Altitude answering hereto.

Gazophilaciō Astronomicū.

Spoud. I praye you geue me example hereof, or you do take in hande any other matters.

Philo. The thing is so easy, as it nede no farther working, yet I will not refuse in so litle a request, to satisfye your desire. I find the sonne, the first day of the new yere 1558, in the signe of the Goate .xx. degrees) the .37. mi-

A TABLE OF THE SONNES MERIDIANE,

Altitude above the Horizont. Calculated for every digree in the Zodiake, Respecting th' Elevation of the Pole Arctike, at Norwich 52. Digrees 10. minutes, & the Sonnes Declination 23. Digrees 28. minutes.

Digr.	Capricornus		Aquarius		Pisces.		Aries.		Taurus.		Gemini.		Dig
	Digr.	Min	Dig	Min	Dig.	Min	Dig	Min	Dig.	Min	Dig.	Min	
0	14	22	17	14	25	36	37	50	50	4	58	26	30
1	14	23	17	26	25	57	38	16	50	26	58	37	29
2	14	23	17	38	26	19	38	42	50	47	58	48	28
3	14	24	17	50	26	42	39	8	51	8	58	58	27
4	14	25	18	3	27	4	39	34	51	28	59	8	26
5	14	27	18	16	27	27	40	0	51	48	59	18	25
6	14	29	18	29	27	50	40	25	52	8	59	27	24
7	14	32	18	43	28	13	40	51	52	28	59	36	23
8	14	35	18	57	28	36	41	17	52	47	59	45	22
9	14	38	19	12	29	0	41	43	53	6	59	53	21
0	14	42	19	27	29	24	42	8	53	25	60	1	20
11	14	46	19	42	29	48	42	34	53	43	60	9	19
12	14	50	19	58	30	12	42	59	54	1	60	16	18
3	14	55	20	14	30	36	43	24	54	19	60	22	17
14	15	0	20	30	31	1	43	49	54	36	60	29	16
5	15	6	20	47	31	26	44	14	54	53	60	34	15
6	15	11	21	3	32	0	44	39	55	10	60	40	14
7	15	18	21	21	32	16	45	4	55	26	60	45	13
8	15	24	21	48	32	41	45	28	55	42	60	50	12
19	15	31	21	56	33	6	45	52	55	58	60	54	11
20	15	39	22	15	33	32	46	16	56	13	60	58	10
21	15	47	22	34	33	57	46	40	56	28	61	2	9
22	15	55	22	52	34	23	47	4	56	43	61	5	8
23	16	4	23	12	34	49	47	27	56	57	61	8	7
24	16	13	23	31	35	15	47	50	57	11	61	11	6
25	16	22	23	51	35	40	48	13	57	24	61	13	5
26	16	32	24	12	36	6	48	36	57	37	61	14	4
27	16	42	24	32	36	32	48	58	57	50	61	16	3
28	16	52	24	53	36	58	49	21	58	2	61	17	2
29	17	3	25	14	37	24	49	43	58	14	61	17	1
30	17	14	25	36	37	50	50	4	58	26	61	18	0
Digr.	Digr.	Min.	Dig.	Min.	Dig.	Min.	Dig.	Min.	Dig.	Min.	Dig.	Min.	Dig
	Sagittarius.		Scorpius.		Libra.		Virgo.		Leo.		Cancer.		

nutes I omit, as not requisite in this businesse) then first
I found in the hier part of the table, Capricornus, therfore I descending downward (in the second columne a-
gainst the .20. degre of Capricorne) founde .15. degrees
39. minuts, the altitude of the sonne for the mids of that
day. In like maner the same yere, the .6. day of Septem-
bre the sonne had his course in the .24. degre of the vir-
gine, and because I finde Virgo in the lower parte of the
Table, ascendinge in the 1ist colunme vpward, find the
24. degre, and against it in the columne of Virgo. 40.
degrees 25. minutes, the Meridian altitude of the sone,
answering that degree: in like sort, do with any degre of
th'other signes, whan as occasion is ministred.

Spou.   This now shall I alway kepe surely in memorye, and because you haue heare apte place to geue me
some precepte for th'eleuation of the Pole Arcticke, I
desire you herein to show me some instructions.

Phi.   I will so do, and the rather for that wythoute it
you can little preuaile in this Arte: and with knowinge
it, and the longitudes of regions, you shall meruclouslye
profit.   Spou.   I praye you then begin firste with the
finding out of the latitude of any place.

Philo.   Whan as the sonne is in either Æquinoctiall
poyntes, by the helpe of your none steade shadowe, you
shal find when he is in the meridian line: then with your
instrument take his altitude, whiche you shall subtracte
from .90. degrees, and the remanent shallbe the iust eleuation of the Pole, as for example.

To finde oute th'eleuation of the Pole aboue the HoriZont.

I.iiij.   At Nor-

An obferua-
tion. At Norwich. 1557, the 10. of march, J found the meridiane altitude of the fone by my Aftrolabe 37. degrees
and 50. minutes, which J did fubtract from 90. degrees,
and there remained 52. degrees 10. minuts, the true
height of the Pole, and latitude of Norwich.
Spou. And do you not marke his declination at that
time? Phi. J cannot marke that, whiche is not. For in
Fol.31. & 32. thefe poynts he hath no declination, and that you might
fe in the table feruing that vfe which is in the firft boke.
But although this way is very perfect, yet carieth it this
difcommoditie with him: that you can but twife yearely,
take th'eleuatiõ of the Pole. And therfore J will fhowe
you alfo how to find it whan he is in the Tropick poynts.
Spoud. That is in the beginning of Cancer and Capricorn. Phi. Jt is fo, you fhall finde oute (as afore) wyth
your inftrument the fonnes height at middaye, whan as
he is in the firft degree of Cancer.
Spou. That time can J finde oute by the helpe of an
Ephemerides. Phi. From this height, you fhall take
away, as your table fheweth 23. degrees 28. minuts : this
numbre you fhall fubtract frõ 90. degrees, & the rema-
nant fhalbe th'exacte Eleuation of your pole, as for example. J find the height of the fone at midday in the beginning of Cancer. 61. degrees. 18. minutes, from which
I take 23. degrees 28. minutes, and there fhall remayne
37. degrees 50. minutes, this nomber J take from. 90.
degrees (being an hole quadrant) there remaineth 52.
degrees 10. minutes, th'eleuation of the pole.
Spoud. J will proue by your licence, and I can do in
like cafe

like cafe whan as he is in Capricorn. Phil. Do you fo.
Spou. I imagine his none fteade heighte to be.14.de-
grees.22.minutes, for becaufe he is farre from our Zenit: from which I cannot fubftract the greateft declination of the fonne, anfwering the firft degre of Capricorn,
in the table of declination. Phi. Nor you fhall not
make anye fubtraction. For like as whan he declineth
North, from th'equinoctiall (which is from the begin- *The Sonnes declinatiõ north.*
ning of Aries vnto th'end of Virgo) you fhall fubtracte
his declinatiõ from his altitude: fo in like maner, hauing
his declination South (which is from the beginninge of *The Sonnes declinatiõ fouth.*
Lybra vnto th'end of Pifces) you mufte adde his decli-
nation to the meridian altitude: and fubtract thẽ bothe
from.90.degrees. Spo. Then I wil end my example.
I do adde.23.degrees.28.min.vnto 14.degrees 22.min.
(the noneftede height) which make 37.degrees.50.mi.
& I take this frõ.90.degrees, as you commaunded, and
ther remaineth 52.degrees.10.minutes as afore.
Phil. You haue truely wrought.
Spou. But is it not poffible to finde th'eleuatiõ of the
Pole euery day? for in traueling it fhuld pleafure me.
Phil. It is poffible to find it not only euery day, but al
fo euery hour: but I will referue that vntill an other fea-
fon, and will fhew you how to find the height of the Pole
euery day, for whiche thinge I will geue you two fondrye
wais: th'one without any other inftrumente more then a
ftaffe, or other thing erected to geue à fhadow (whyche I
haue inuented) th'other way is by the helpe of an inftru- *The third way*
ment, with which I will begin. Take the fonnes heighte
as be-

as before beinge in the Meridian line, then take oute of some Ephemerides his place in the Zodiake, in degrees, & minutes, with which you shall enter into the table of declination, & ther find his declination from th'Equinoctiall, answering to the said degrees, & minutes. And if it be North, thē subtracte it from th'Altitude Meridiā: or if it be South, adde it to the said Altitude : then addyng, or subtracting that numbre from 90. Digrees, there shall remayne the trewe Eleuation of the Pole.

Spoud.   Wyll it please you to let me proue this rule by an example?   Philo.   Right gladly.

Spou.   I finde the Sonne in the sixt Digree of Gemini, whose heighte as you see is 59. Digrees 28. minutes, well nye. And nowe I finde in the Table of the Sonnes declination vnder the 6. Digree of Gemini. 21. Digrees. 37. minutes 58. secondes. Whiche I subtracting from the sonnes height, ther doth remaine 37. digrees 50. minutes, this I take from 90. digrees, & finde the place in height 52. digrees 10. minutes.

Phil.   Let not this slide out of your memory, because it hath a singuler vse in this art, & by it you may in al places wher you trauaile, finde out the height of the Pole.

The. 4. way.   And nowe I will shewe you my waye howe to finde th'aforesaide eleuation.

Spou.   And shall your way serue in like maner for euery day in the yeare?

Phi.   I find out the height of the North starre by the shadow ether. iiij. times in the yere, or els euery day the sonne being in the meridian line.

Spou.

Spou. *Then I require you shew me first howe to finde the latitude of any Citie or towne.*

Philon. *right willingly. You shall prouide a staffe , or any right wand, in what length you please, this you shall deuide into. 60. equall portions. Then take oute of some Ephemerides, or Almanach, the day whan as the Sone entreth into the first digree of Aries, Cancer, Libra, & Capricornus. At which times set your staffe vpright in some place: And marke the shadow how longe it doth decrease, & whā it is at the shortest, the sone is in the noon stead place. Then at that instaunt take the length of the shadow, & enter into the Tablé of shadowes : & there thou shalt finde th'exacte Latitude of thy Citie. As for thy better instruction: I find in an Ephemerides the sone to be in the firste Digree of Aries, 1558. the 12. daye of March. Therfore whan as the sonne approche towarde the south, I set my staffe directly vp , & find the shadow at midday 77. parts, 13. minutes, with which I enter the Table of shadowes (vnder this title, Æquinoctiall shadow) & can not finde my number expressed, therfore I finde next vnder my nūber seuentie sixe, 48. vnto which 52. digrees in Latitude do answere, wherfore I workinge by proportion, finde correspondent vnto 77. parts, 13. minutes: 52. digrees, 10. minutes.*

Spoud. *Then your minde is, that I shall vse the rule of proportion, in all Tables, where as the perfect nūber is not expresedly founde.* Philo. *Yea certainly.*

Spo. *Now shew how I may work euery day the same coclusiō.* Phi. *It differeth in no point frō the former*

order

order, sauinge that in the table of shadowes, you muste only haue respect to the columne of the sonnes altitude, & the shadow answering hereto. Then to finde the degre he is in at that present: next in the table of declination to seke out the declination of the same degree, & if it be North, subtract it from the altitude, so the remanent from. 90. degrees, & you shall haue your owne desire.   Spoud.   But & J finde him to decline Southe, must J adde it to his altitude, & subtract both from. 90 degrees, as you did in the other?

The astronomie Ringe.

Philo.   Jn the same maner in all poyntes. There is also an other waye to finde the latitude of Regions and Cities by the helpe of the Astronomy Ringe, whiche you shall finde in my boke touching that matter, in whiche J shew the making, as also th'use of the same.

Spou.   But in the night seaso, how may J find the said Eleuation of the Pole in anye place.

Philo.   The Mariners vse to find out the latitude of the place by findinge the height of the Northe starre, which they call the lode starre, esteming à degre, or two, in obseruation as no error. But you shall worcke in thys maner: first find out any notable starre (that you knowe perfaitly) in the table of fixed starres, & with Ptolomæus rule, or other instrumente, obserue his heighte in the meridian line: then in the table of declination, you shall find how much he declineth North or South, from th'equinoctiall, & obseruing th'order, as you do with the searching out of the Pole by the sonnes altitude Meridiane, and declination: you shall haue your hole desire.
                                                    Spou.

Spou. *Will you nowe shewe the findyng out of the Lõgitude of any place from the Canariane Ilandes?*

Philo. *It is not so easie, & facile à thing, to trie th'eleuation of the Pole: but it is as harde, & laborus, to get the Longitude, which was the cause that the Auncient Geographers had onely one way, & that is by obseruing of th'Eclipses of the Mone.*

Spoud. *I remember Strabo affirmith the same.*　　*Lib.1.fol.6.*

Phi. *There is in dede no way so parfit, & suer, as by th'Eclises: therfore king Atreus is worthy eternall fame, which was the finder out of th'Eclipses of the Sonne, & Mone, (1205. yeares before Christ our Sauiours incarnation) by whose trauaile we receaue this benefite.*　*Atreus found first oute the time of Eclipses.*

Spoud. *Not we only, that are presetly liuing: but also such as haue bene before vs, & also those that shall here after folowe. But what is the cause of hyr obscuration, doeth not she at that time lose in dede hyr light?*

Phi. *No, verely: For it is directly against Aristotle, & all Philosophers well neare, to confesse that the supercelestiall bodies are subiect to alteration, yea or to affirme, anye coloure in them. But I wil let that passe, & wil show you the cause of her eclipsing, which is no other thing, thē the mone being (in oppositiõ of the sõne) ether in the hed or tail of the dragõ: the shadow of th'erth is betwixt the mone, & our sight. So that as longe as she is in perfit oppositiõ & without latitude, so lõg doth she cõtinue in darknes. Spo. And is she not Eclipsed at no other time then only at the Ful? Phil. No certeinly & therfore Lucan doth aptly in his first boke opē the cause, &*　*Aristotle.*　*The cause of the mone Eclipsed.*

K.j.　　time

time of the mones Eclipsation, in these versis.

― Cornuq; coacto,
Iam Phæbe toto fratrem cum redderet Orbe,
Terrarum subita percussa expalluit vmbra.

VVhan as the mone vnto the world, her brother Titan bright
In forme wold represent, shining with face both full and round:
She sodenly was sore wounded, and therwith left her light,
Titan causing th'earthes shadow, her beauty to confound.

Spou. *These verses are short, & very full of eloquēce.*

Phil. *Yea & they are also easy to be vndarstand, for she neuer resembleth the figure of the sonne (whō Poëts call her brother) but only whā she is at the ful, at which time beinge in th'opposite place to him, th'earthe (as J saide) shadoweth her from oure sightes. But let that passe, and beholde to serue thy vse in this behalf, I haue calculated such Eclipses of the mone, as shall happē frō the yeare of oure Lorde. 1560. vntill the yere. 1605: Applying the time of ther beginning, in yeares, daies, houres, & minuts, vnto the meridiā of Norwich ex- actly, whiche is.22.degrees, and.30.minuts, from the Canarian, or West fortunate Ilandes.*

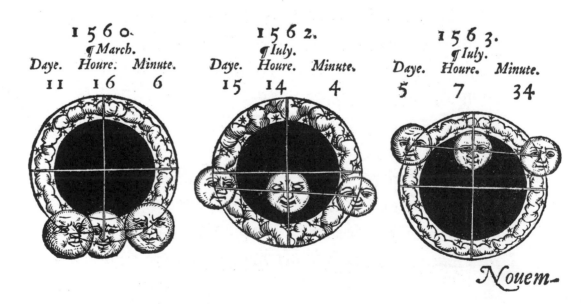

1 5 6 0.			1 5 6 2.			1 5 6 3.		
¶ March.			¶ Iuly.			¶ Iuly.		
Daye.	Houre.	Minute.	Daye.	Houre.	Minute.	Daye.	Houre.	Minute.
11	16	6	15	14	4	5	7	34

Nouem-

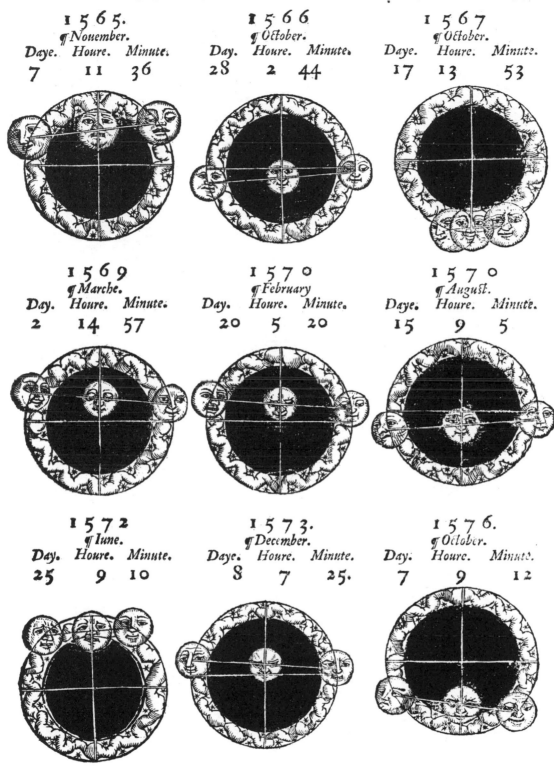

1 5 6 5. ¶ Nouember.			1 5 6 6 ¶ October.			1 5 6 7 ¶ October.		
Daye.	Houre.	Minute.	Day.	Houre.	Minute.	Daye.	Houre.	Minute.
7	11	36	28	2	44	17	13	53

1 5 6 9 ¶ Marche.			1 5 7 0 ¶ February			1 5 7 0 ¶ August.		
Day.	Houre.	Minute.	Day.	Houre.	Minute.	Daye.	Houre.	Minute.
2	14	57	20	5	20	15	9	5

1 5 7 2 ¶ Iune.			1 5 7 3. ¶ December.			1 5 7 6. ¶ October.		
Day.	Houre.	Minute.	Daye.	Houre.	Minute.	Day.	Houre.	Minute.
25	9	10	8	7	25.	7	9	12

K ij. Aprill

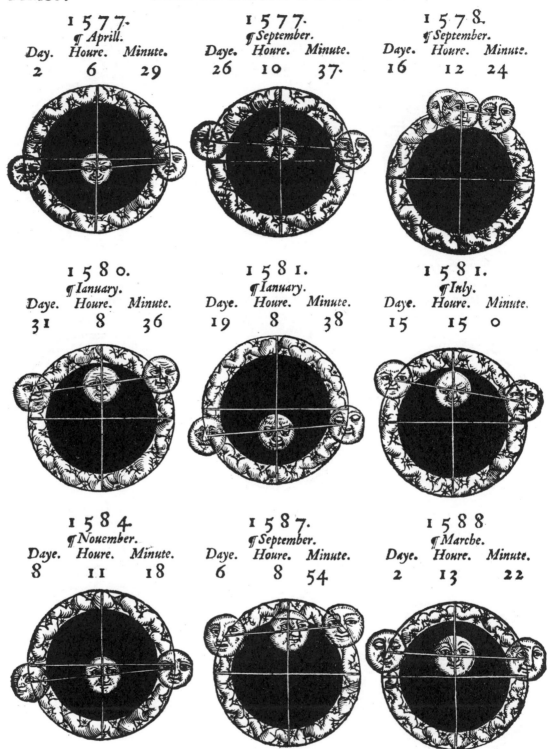

1 5 7 7.
¶ Aprill.
Day.   Houre.   Minute.
2   6   29

1 5 7 7.
¶ September.
Daye.   Houre.   Minute.
26   10   37.

1 5 7 8.
¶ September.
Daye.   Houre.   Minute.
16   12   24

1 5 8 0.
¶ Ianuary.
Daye.   Houre.   Minute.
31   8   36

1 5 8 1.
¶ Ianuary.
Daye.   Houre.   Minute.
19   8   38

1 5 8 1.
¶ Irly.
Daye.   Houre.   Minute.
15   15   0

1 5 8 4
¶ Nouember.
Daye.   Houre.   Minute.
8   11   18

1 5 8 7.
¶ September.
Daye.   Houre.   Minute.
6   8   54

1 5 8 8
¶ Marche.
Daye.   Houre.   Minute.
2   13   22

August

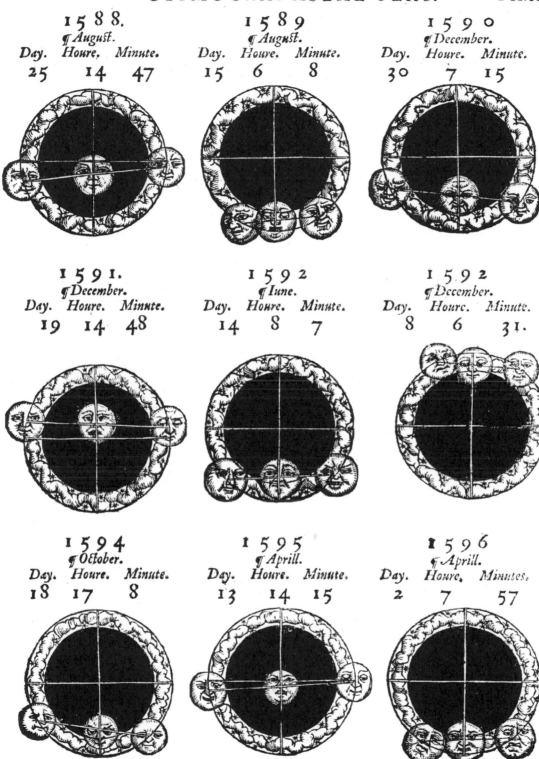

1588. ¶August.		
Day.	Houre.	Minute.
25	14	47

1589 ¶August.		
Day.	Houre.	Minute.
15	6	8

1590 ¶December.		
Day.	Houre.	Minute.
30	7	15

1591. ¶December.		
Day.	Houre.	Minute.
19	14	48

1592 ¶Iune.		
Day.	Houre.	Minute.
14	8	7

1592 ¶December.		
Day.	Houre.	Minute.
8	6	31.

1594 ¶October.		
Day.	Houre.	Minute.
18	17	8

1595 ¶Aprill.		
Day.	Houre.	Minute.
13	14	15

1596 ¶Aprill.		
Day.	Houre.	Minutes.
2	7	57

K iij.

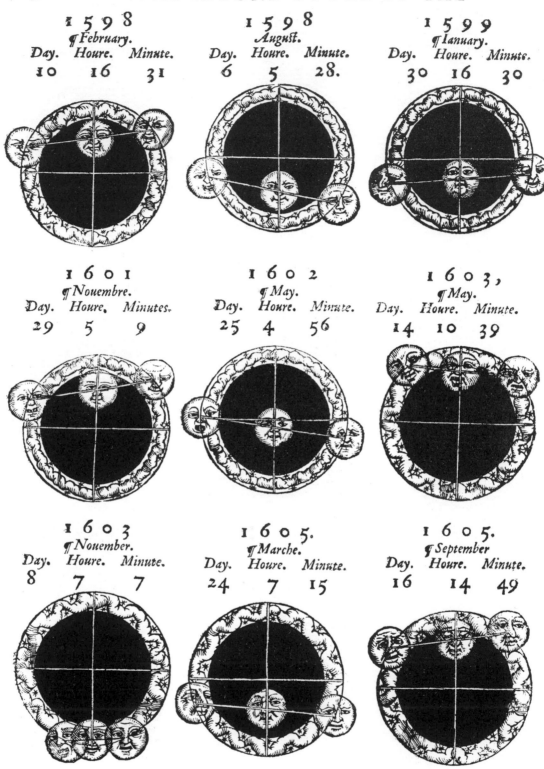

1 5 9 8
¶ February.
Day.　Houre.　Minute.
10　16　31

1 5 9 8
August.
Day.　Houre.　Minute.
6　5　28.

1 5 9 9
¶ Ianuary.
Day.　Houre.　Minute.
30　16　30

1 6 0 1
¶ Nouembre.
Day.　Houre.　Minutes.
29　5　9

1 6 0 2
¶ May.
Day.　Houre.　Minute.
25　4　56

1 6 0 3,
¶ May.
Day.　Houre.　Minute.
14　10　39

1 6 0 3
¶ Nouember.
Day.　Houre.　Minute.
8　7　7

1 6 0 5.
¶ Marche.
Day.　Houre.　Minute.
24　7　15

1 6 0 5.
¶ September
Day.　Houre.　Minute.
16　14　49

Whan

Whan as thou wilt finde the longitude of any Region, Country, or Village, by an Eclipse, do in this manner. Obserue diligently the perfaite time, whan as she beginneth to be eclipsed (either by some perfait Dial, or clock, or els by the heighte of some fixed sterre) and if the time of hyr beginninge, do agree with that whiche thou shalt find here calculated, know certainly that thy Meridian and longitud, is all one with Norwich: but if they differ, do in this order. Subtract the lesser time, from oute of the greater, & the differēce turn into degrees, & mi. of the Equinoctial. Thē if the time in the beginning of her obscuration be more, then that which J haue heare placed: adde this difference in degrees, and minuts, vnto the lōgitude of Norwiche, (because the place is East from it, and you shall haue the perfait lōgitude. But and she begin soner with the, to be Eclipsed then is here mētioned, subtract the difference aforesaid in digrees & minuts, from the Longitude of Norwiche (because thou arte West from it) & you shal haue the Longitude desired.

Spou.   Howe shall I torne the houres, & minutes of the day into digrees, & minutes of th'Equinoctiall?

Philo.   You must giue to euery houre, 15. digrees: & to euery 4. minu. of an houre, one digr. of th'Equinoctial: & euery minu. of an houre, 15. minu. of th'Equinoctiall: as this Table folowyng shall alway declare. And nowe I wyll giue you à twofould example. Anno. Christi. 1558. the second day of Aprill, there was à great Eclipse of the Mone, so that she was darkened x. pointes well nere, & began to come vnder the shadowe of th'Earth at Norwiche,

Howe to finde the Longitude of Regions by an Eclypse.

How to turne the houres of the daye into degrees & minuces.

An obseruation of an Eclipse.

K iiij.

wich, at x. a clock 37. minutes at night (as by taking the height of à fixed sterre, called the virgins spike, did euidently appeare) now willing to note mens obseruations in other places, I finde that *Leouitius Cyprianus*, in hys boke of Eclipses, apoynteth it to begin at *Augusta* in *Ger*many 23. min. after xi. a clock at night. Then to find the longitude of *Augusta* frō *Norwich* I subtract .x. houres 37. min. frō xi, houres 23 min, ther remaine 49, minuts,

A TABLE, SERVING TO THE CON=
uerting the houres, and minutes of the day: into digrees, and minutes of th'Equinoctiall.

Hou. of the day	Th'ark of th'equinoctiall in				Mi. of hou.	Th'arke of th'Equinoctiall in			
	Digre.	Mi	Second			Digrees	Min.	Secō.	Third.
1	15	2	30		1	0	15	2	3
2	30	5	0		2	0	30	5	0
3	45	7	30		3	0	45	7	30
4	60	10	0		4	0	0	10	0
5	75	12	30		5	1	15	12	30
6	90	15	0		6	1	30	15	0
7	105	17	30		7	1	45	17	30
8	120	20	0		8	2	0	20	0
9	135	22	30		9	2	15	22	30
10	150	25	0		10	2	30	25	0
11	165	27	30		15	3	45	37	30
12	180	30	0		20	3	0	50	0
13	195	32	30		25	6	16	12	30
14	201	35	0		30	7	31	15	0
15	225	37	30		35	8	46	27	30
16	240	40	0		40	10	1	49	0
17	255	42	30		45	11	17	1	30
18	270	45	0		50	12	32	5	0
19	285	47	30		55	13	48	2	30
20	300	50	0		60	15	2	30	0
21	315	52	30						
22	330	55	0						
23	345	57	30						
24	361	0	0						

with which I enter into this table, & finde answeringe
to.46.minutes of time.11.degrees.30. minu.of th'equinoctiall, & because that the beginning of the Eclipse, is
later at Augusta, then at Norwich, it sheweth the situation to be East from it.Wherfore I adde the difference
of time tourned into degrees vnto 22.degrees 30.minu.
(the longitud of Norwich) & ther ariseth.34.degrees
the longitude of Augusta.In like manner 1559.the.xvi.
day of September, at 3.of the clock 19.min.after dinner,
the mone shall begin to be darckened at Norwich, whiche at Tolet in Spain shall happen at 2.of the clocke.22.
minutes.The difference in time is 47.minuts.I conuert
them into degrees, & minutes of th'equinoctiall(as before) & finde 11.degreet 50.min.And because that the
Mone is darkned soner at Tolet, then Norwich, I subtract this difference frō Norwich & finde.10.degrees,
40.minutes, the longitude of Tolet which is West from
Norwich. Spo.   But this Eclipse of the Mone, shall
not be sene in the beginning, nether ende at Norwiche,
or Tolet?   Phi.   True it is, because the Mone being
in the perfit opposition of the sonne, can not shew her self
aboue our Horizont, before the sone be vnder th'Earth,
which is not vnto.6.of the clocke.
Spou.   How can you then shew the true time of her beginning at Norwiche, or Tolet, whan as she is not sene
of their inhabitauntes? Philo.   right perfetlye . Con-
ferring the meridian of Norwich, or Tolet, wyth other
places East from them , whereas the beginninge shallbe
plainly of these inhabitants perceiued.But in this place
it is

it is broughte in onlye for example. And althoughe thys waye of finedinge the true longitude be bothe certain, and mooste easiest of all other : yet it hathe this discomodity, becaufe th'eclipses happen rarely, and seldom, as twise in à yere at the most, & sumtime but once in.ij. yere. Furthermore ther hapeneth sumtime impedimēts that at the time also of her Eclipsing, we cannot obserue her beginning or end, either becaufe the cloudes are betwixt our sight, & her, & so is shadowed: or els that she is vnder our Horizont, at that presēt seafon. Wherfore

Apians waye to find out the Longitude of places. P. Apiā practised an other way, how to find out th'aforesaid Longitude, yea & that euery night & hour of the same, so that the Mone be aboue the Horizont, & the aire cleare and faire.

Spou. We are bound to haue him in much estimatiō, which by his labours, hathe supplied that we did wante: but what is his inuention? Phil. J will shew you, ther

Iacobes staffe. are thre thinges required vnto this busines, the Astronomers staffe, also called Iacobes staffe (the makinge of which you shall finde among th'other instrumentes) the second is the true place of the Mone in the Zodiake, in degrees, & minutes, for the hour you make obseruatiō, (whiche you may take out of an Ephemerides) and the iij. is the longitude of a fixed sterre, which you may take

Fol.27. out of the Table of fixed sterres in my firste boke. These had, you muste take your staffe with the Crosse on it. and applye the one ende of the Crosse to the Center of the Mone, and the other vnto the sterre: which thing to do, you shall remoue the Crosse vp and downe, vntill

th'endes

the endes of the staffe touch both the center of the mone
& also of the sterre. Thys ended, the crosse shall shewe
you what the distaunce of the Mone, & starre is in degrees & minutes. Then take the distaunce in degrees,
& minuts of the Mone, & fixed sterre, which you had
before the obseruation: And substract these. ij. distances,
th'one out of th'other, the remanet deuide by the portiõ
that the mone moueth in one hour, And that shall shew
you the time, whan as the Mone was ioyned wyth the
starre (if the starre be West from her) or whan she shall
be ioyned with the starre, if it be East from the Mone.
This time being had, you shall turne it into degrees, &
minutes of th'equinoctiall, (as I said in th'other precept
afore, & the table sheweth) & if the mone be West of
the starre, do in this manner. Marcke whether the difference of the mone, & starre found by thy obseruation,
be greater then the difference foũd by the ephemerides,
& the lõgitude of the fixed starre: if it be lesser, thẽ subtract the time turned into degrees, & mi. from the meridian for whiche th'Ephemerides are Calculated,
because thy place is west from it: but and the difference
be greater, then adde the degrees, & mi. to the Longitude (for which th'Ephemerides ar supputated, because
thy place is East from it) & so shalt thou haue the true
Longitude desired. Moreouer thou must consider if the
Mone be East frõ the Sterre, then thou shalt worke contrary (that is to say) if the distaũce found by obseruatiõ,
be lesser thẽ th'other, you shall subtract it frõ the lõgitud
knowẽ, because thi place is west frõ it, but & this differẽce

be

Whan the
Mone is West
of the Starre
What is to be
wrought.

Whã the mone
is Easte of the
Sterre.

be greater, then adde it to the fornamed Longitude, because thy place is East from th'other: & so withoute erroure, thou shalt haue thine owne desire. And this waye also, is excellente to correcte the course of the Mone, and amend the tables, out of which hir mouinges are taken: if they do erre at any time. Spo. I must neades confesse your words true, whã you said how much any thing excelled other in knowledge, so much the more it was cõpanion with difficultie. For except you geue me an exãple, I shall neuer attain the perfait meaning hereof. Philon. I will geue you an exãple of that time, which I obserued my self to find out the lõgitude of Norwich.

An example, Anno.1558.the second day of February, at.x.a clocke at night, I found the place of regulus (called also the lions hart) in longitude degrees.23.32.minut.in Leo: the Mone also at that present, in the.xxi.degree.xl.min.of the same signe (hir place being calculated for Anwarp, which is xxvi.degrees.xxxvj.minutes) I subtracte the place of the mone, from the longitude of regulus, the distance.j.degre.lij.min.that she is West, from the sterre. Then I take my staffe & (with one eie closed) I moue the crosse vp & down, vntill th'one end was equall with the Center of the Mone, th'other ende with the Starre. Then I find by that obseruation, the Mone to differ frõ regulus, j.degree.43.min.This numbre I take from the first difference, ther remaineth 9.minutes.Thẽ inquire I out, how many min.of time, answer vnto.9.min.of the Mones course, (making the Mone to moue in one hour xxxv.minutes, & find.xvj.minutes of time: which turned

ned into degrees of th'equinoctiall, make. 4. degrees: &
becauſe the Mone is Weſt of the ſterre, & the diſtance
found by the ſtaffe leſſe in number, therefore I ſubtracte
the. 4. degrees from the longitude of Anwarpe, & there
remaine. 22. degrees. 36. minutes, which differ littel frõ
the other obſeruations.

Spou.　The difference of. 6. minutes in Longitude, is
ſmall or no error, whan as. 15. minutes of th'equinoctiall,
make but one minute of time.

Phil.　True it is.

Spoud.　By youre exãple, the precept ſemeth more euident, & J miſtruſte not, but with diligence to make in
other places, the like obſeruation.

Phi.　I will open vnto you an other waye to finde the ┌Another waye.┐
Longitude of any region, in euery place, as well daye, as
night, & that euery houre, moſt neceſſary for thẽ, which
either ſayle, or trauell.

Spou. But you do then obſerue the diſtaunce of the places, in miles.

Phil.　No verely, for if I were caried by lande into
places vnknowẽ (blindfilded, as they terme it) or by the
violence of troubleſome wether, on the ſea, driuen from
my courſe, J can declare how many miles I am from my
countrey, & how many leaques from my proper courſc.

Spoud.　Then ſurely, it muſt haue in it muche difficultie, ſeyng that there ſpringeth of it ſo muche vtilitie,
and profite.

Philo.　The waye is very facile, & without great laboure, & J will no lenger make you muſe theron.

　　　　　　　　　　L i.　　　　　You

You shall prepare à parfait clocke artificially made, such
as are brought from Flaūders, & we haue thē as excellently without Temple barre, made of our countrymen.
Spoud.   Do you not meane such, as we vse to weare in
the facion of à Tablet? Phi.   Yea truely, when as you
trauell, you shall set the nedle of youre Diall exactlye on
the hour found out by the sonne on the daye, & by some
starre in the night:thē traueling withoute intermission,
whan as you haue traueled.xx.yea.xl.miles or more (if
your next place, whose longitude you desire be so far distant)then marke in your Diall, the houre that it shew-
eth:after with an Astrolabe, or Quadrant, finde out the
hour of the day in that place: & if it agre with the same
which your clock sheweth, be assured your place is north
or South frō the place you came from , & therfore haue
the same lōgitude, & meridiā line. But & the time dif
fer, subtract th'one, out of th'other, & the differēce turn
into degrees & minut.of th'equinoctiall as before , then
adde or subtract, as in th'other.ij.precepts, going before.
But now behold the skie is ouer cast with cloudes:
wherfore let vs haste to our lodgings, &
ende our talke for this presente.
Spoud.   With a righte
good will.

THE THIRD BOOKE OF THE

Cosmographicall Glasse: in which is vttered the making and protracture, of the Face of th' Earth, both in Cartes Perticuler, and also vniuersall, with diuers necessarye thinges, incidente hereto.

Philonicus.

EINGE THAT in oure laste daies talke, it was made euidente vnto you, what the Longitude, Latitude, & Circuite of th' Earth was, how you also might find the same by diuers & sondrye waies: moreouer the deuision of th' Earth into zones, by the helpe of Paralleles : it shuld seme nowe conueniente, to shewe you the cause wherefore all these are learned, & to what finall end they are desired. Therfore, leaste you shulde be lefte destitute of the principal tresure of Cosmography, that is to delineat, protract, or set forth the plat forme of th' vniuersall face of th' earth: or els perticulerli any one portiõ of the same: J will this day also do my endeuor, to shewe you the waye how to attain hereunto. Spo. Wold to god, that fortune had vnto me geuẽ of her tresure, that I might sõwhat (although not recõpẽce) yet shew forth my good wil for this your great pains, & trauell. For in dede siluer & gold, is to base to recõpence knowledge with, & that did the famous kinges & princes in th' old time well perpende:

The principall part of Cosmographie.

The noble rewarde, of learnyng in times paste.

L.ij.   Whan

Whan they did not only geue th'inuentors (of any new
Science, Art, or profitable thing for à publike weale)a-
boundaunce of treasure : but also for perpetuall memorye, made an Image to represente suche à persone, and
Neptunus. called him à God for his inuention. So was Neptunus called God of the seas, for that he founde the Arte
of sayling. Æolus, the God of windes, because he inuen-
Æolus. ted the true vse of them. Ceres à Goddesse, for finedinge
Ceres. out tillage. But what make I discourse in these thinges
to you, whiche knowe them muche better then I.

Ph.   Heare by, I gather your good will to th'aduance-
mente of learning. But it is not treasure which at youre
handes I craue, but only that you shew your selfe enemy
vnto ignoraunce, thorowe your industrious labour, both
in profitinge your selfe, & also your natiue country.
But or we procede further in thys oure busynesse, I wyll
brieflye open vnto you certaine names, whiche we vse in
Geographie, with th'interpretation of the same: and histories with Poëtes abound also with them. And firste
you muste consider that th'Earthe beinge inuironed, &
compassed aboute with the greate Ocian seas, semeth
as it were an Ilande (after Strabo his minde)notwith-
standinge there is à greate difference betwixt an Iland,
What an I- and th'Earthe: for an Ilande, is a portion of th'Earthe
lande is. seperated from the hole, by waters whiche do circuite it
on euerye side, so that you can not iourney by lande, either from Europe, Asia, or Afrike vnto your coũtry, but
muste vse herein Nauigation.

Spou.

Spoud.   *Vnto your defcription do agree, America, Si-cilia, Iaua, the Rodes, Candie, Delos, Therafia, and England, in which we inhabite.*

Philon.   *It it true, now you fhall furder note that the feas deuide th' Earth. 4. fundry waies, for either it is an Iland, or little differing there from (and therfore cal-led Peninfula) or Ifthmus, or Contines.*

Spoud.   *So that Peninfula, differeth from an* Peninfula.
Ilande, becaufe in fome parte, it is ioyned to à greater portion of th' Earth wythoute feperation : as Taurica, Thrafia, Cherronefus, alfo Cymbrica & Aurea, in India.

Philo.   *Ifthmus, doeth differ from them bothe* Ifthmus.
& fignifieth à portion of th' Earthe, hauynge of eyther fydes the raginge Seas : fuche are founde agreable to this defcription properly, Corinthiacus, and Thra-fius.

Spou.   *But howe doeth Continens differ from thefe* Continent.
three?

Ph.   *I will fhew you, it is à portiõ of th' Earth, which is not parted by the Seas à founder, but is continually in length, fo that you may go from one parte vnto another without nauigation : as Saxonie, Bohemie, Sueuelande, &c.*

Spod.   *By thefe I gather there is no portion of th' Earth, but it is either an Ilande, or that whiche you call Peninfula, Ifthmus, or Continens.*

Philon. *No verely, but nowe beholde the figure. Yet ther remaineth to fhew you what this worde, Ōceā Sea, meaneth, what we call Promontorium, Fretum, Lacus, Stagnum, Fluuius, Palus, &c. which I referue vntill we fpeake of Nauigation: And nowe we will tourne to our fcope. You fhall cōfider that the face of th'Earth is protrafte, & drawne two fundry waies: either on à roūd plate forme, for which inuention the Globe mofte aptlye ferueth: or els on à plaine plat forme, as à Card in which we drawe th'vniuerfall Earth, or els but the half, or the one part: yea, & you pleafe but one particuler Region: which is proper to Chorographie (as I faid to you in the firft booke. Spo. Th'inuention fhould feme much bet-*

ter to drawe th'Earth in à playne plate fourme, theron à Globe, for in it, we maye behoulde the whole face

An obiection
againft the te
reftriall
Globe.

of

of th'Earthe, wythout anye remouynge or tournynge
of the Carde: & on the Globe you ſhall be compelled to
turne firſte one parte, & then another, or you can vew
any great portion of it.

Phil.   Yet becauſe it doeth moſt euidently in figure, *Th'Anſwere.*
repreſent the forme of th'Earth, it ſhould ſeme more apt
for this inſtitution. But I will leaue his compoſition vntill I ſhewe you the making of it among other inſtrumē-
tes. And your cauſe alleaged againſt this forme, as I ſuppoſe, did miniſter occation to Ptolomæus, to delineat, &
deſcribe th'Earth in à plaine forme. And bicauſe that
right lines onely vſed in this buſines, did cary errour
with them (as the fornamed Ptolomæus noted in Marinus the Geographers inuention) therefore he vſed in
this protraction, ſuche lines as might anſwere proporti-
onallye, the lines diſcribed in a Globe: But nowe I will
leaue to vſe more wordes herein, & will begin the work
it ſelf. And leaſt that the difficultie of the thing mighte
ſomwhat diſcouragie you, I will firſt noſel & traine you
vp in making a cart for à Region. But here note that à *A particuler*
carde, made.ij.
waies.
perticuler card is made by knowing the diſtance of pla-
ces: without Longitude & Latitude of Regions, which
forme of working J wyll here after open: or by Longitudes, with which firſte we will begin. And then ſhewe you
the making of à Carde, for the eight part of th'Earth, af- *The argument*
of the thirde
booke.
ter for halfe th'Earth, & laſt for the hole vniuerſal face
of th'Earth.   Spoud. J thanke you ſir, & nowe J
perceiue your great care in obſeruing à methode, & order in teaching, with the manifolde vtilitie ſpringing of

L.iiij.   the

the same: But seing you wil begin first with the descrip-
sion of à Regiō, I pray you let your diligence that waye
bende, to the settyng out of our countrey. So shall the example be the more familier, & your paines nothing the
greater.

Phil.   I wyll accōplish your desire, in describinge à perticuler Regiō, Countrey, or Prouince, Firste you shall
drawe à right line in such length (in the middes of your
parchement, or paper) as it will aptly receiue. This line
shall represent the meridiā Line for the middes of that
Regiō. Then diuide this line into so many equal portiōs,
as the latitude of the regiō is: drawynge right Lines, or
paralleles, in euery of the same diuisiōs, according to the
capacitie of the plat forme of thy paper, or parchement,
& write on th'endes of these paralleles, 32. 33. 34. or 40.
41. 42. according to their distaunce frō th'Equinoctall.
after you shall cōsider howe many digrees the north part
of your regiō is frō th'equinoctiall, & entringe into this
Table folowing (which is intituled the quātitie & proportiō of th'Equinoctall, or any great Circle, vnto euerye
parallele both North and Southe from them) searche
how many minutes, and secondes answereth to the furdest of these degrees in latitude, & with thy compasse,
take the like space in anye of the diuisions of latitude:
and then beginninge at the hier parte of the Carte (for
that shall represente the Northe parte) make prickes
with thys compasse from the Meridiane line, on bothe
fides:

The maner of making a per- ticuler Carte for any Regiō.

A PROFITABLE TABLE, SHOVVING THE
quantitie, and proportion of th'Equinoctiall, vnto euerye
Parallele, both towarde the Pole Arctick, & Antarctick,
making euery digree 60.minutes.

Latitude of Paralleles.				Latitude of Paral.				Latitude of paral.			
Dig.	Mi.	Se.	Thir	Dig	M	S.	T.	De.	Mi.	Sec.	Th.
0	60	0	0	31	51	25	48	62	28	10	6
1	59	59	27	32	50	52	58	63	27	14	22
2	59	57	18	33	50	19	13	64	26	18	8
3	59	55	4	34	49	44	32	65	25	21	26
4	59	51	14	35	49	8	57	66	24	24	15
5	59	46	18	36	48	32	28	67	23	26	38
6	59	40	17	37	47	55	5	68	22	28	35
7	59	33	10	38	47	16	50	69	21	30	7
8	59	24	58	39	46	37	44	70	20	31	16
9	59	15	41	40	45	57	46	71	19	32	3
10	59	5	18	41	45	16	57	72	18	32	28
11	58	53	51	42	44	35	19	73	17	32	23
12	58	41	20	43	43	52	52	74	16	32	18
13	58	27	20	44	43	9	37	75	15	31	45
14	58	13	4	45	42	25	35	76	14	30	55
15	57	57	20	46	41	40	46	77	13	29	49
16	57	40	33	47	40	55	12	78	12	28	29
17	57	22	42	48	40	8	52	79	11	26	55
18	57	3	48	49	39	21	49	80	10	25	8
19	56	43	52	50	38	34	2	81	9	23	10
20	56	22	54	51	37	45	33	82	8	21	1
21	56	0	53	52	36	56	23	83	7	18	44
22	55	37	52	53	36	0	32	84	6	16	18
23	55	13	49	54	35	16	2	85	5	13	45
24	54	48	46	55	34	24	53	86	4	11	7
25	54	22	42	56	33	33	6	87	3	8	25
26	53	55	40	57	32	40	42	88	2	5	38
27	53	27	37	58	31	47	43	89	1	2	50
28	52	58	37	59	30	54	8	90	0	0	0
29	52	28	38	60	30	0	0				
30	51	57	4	61	29	5	19				

both fides: then accompte howe farre diftaunte the fouth
parte of thy Region is from th'Equinoctiall, & by the
helpe of the Table you fhall knowe howe many minutes
anfwereth to one digree: then with your copaffe take the
like proportion of the digrees of Latitude, & your compaffe not opened wider, make prickes from either fyde of
the meridian line in the lower part of the Carde, for that
fignifieth the fouth coaft of that regio. After draw right
lines from the prickes in the hier part of the Table, vnto the Prickes in the lower part. And write in them the
degrees of Longitude, as.10.11.12.or.20.21.22.& then
is thy carde made ready to ferue thy neceffary vfe.

Spou. This beinge ended, what is then requifite to be
obferued to the perfait finifhing of this carde?

Phil. Only to feeke oute of Ptolomæus Geographie, or
my fifth booke, the latitudes of Cities, Townes, Villages,
Hilles, Riuers, or other notable thinges in that Region
conteined, & accordinge to thofe nobres, to place the in
your card, or mappe. Spou. I do not fo muche fanfye
Ptolomæus, in logitudes & latitudes, for he was not a-
ble being fo mighty à Prince to trauell into thofe coun-
tris, that to à priuate perfon (for the greate diftaunce à
funder) was impoffible. And therfore receiuinge (as he
confeffeth) obferuations at other mens handes, dyd in
many fundry places fwarue from the trueth.

Ptolomæus ex
cufed. Ph. And that was not to be imputed vnto Ptolomæus
as à crime, feyng the errour enfued by other mens obferuations. But for this caufe I haue made my fifthe
Booke, in the whiche, I haue folowed Ptolomæus in
certeine

certaine pointes touchinge his natiue Countrey, & places to them adiacent. In th'other, I haue vsed later writers trauelles, not omitting my owne as you shall euidēt-
ly perceaue.

Spoudeus.   I pray you giue me an example of these
thinges spoken.

Phil.   Here minding to describe the plat forme of An example
Englande, I draw (as you se) à right line in the middes
of the Mappe. And becauseI finde in my fift bokē, that
it is frō the Weast part of the same to th'East. 11. digres:
I diuide this streght line (beynge the Meridian Line,
for the middes of this Regiō) into xj. equall partes, or
portions: Then do I searche how much the Pole Arctik
is eleuated aboue th'Æquinoctiall, in the furdest north
part of Englande: & finde it 61. (for vnder the name
of Englande, I comprehend the whole Ilande cōteyning
also Schotlande, & Irelande.) Therfore I enter into
the Table goyng before, & finde answering to 61. digr.
29. minutes, 5. secondes, 19. thirdes. Which space, I take
with my cōpasse in one of the diuisiōs of Lōgitude, that
I made in the meridian line, & so my compasse not opened wider, I begin at the Meridian Line in the higher
part of the Card, & make on either side 5. pricks (that is
to sai) v. on the left hād, & v. on the right hād. in like mā
ner I find the south part to differ frō th'equinoctial lj. di.
wherfore entring into the Table, I find answering to lj.
dig: 37. min. 45. seco. 33. thir. And with my cōpasse I take
the like portion in one of the diuisions of the Meridian
line, & then with my compasse I diuide the lower parte.

of

of the Table, as I did the hier. Then draw I right Lines from the Prickes in the hier part of the Table, vnto the prickes in the lower part: & wright at th'endes of them, the Digrees of Lōgitude, as alſo in the diuiſiōs of the Meridiam line, I wright the digrees of latitude. Thē ſeke I in the fifth boke for the notable Cities, Townes, Villages, & ſuche like, & place them in this card, according to their true Longitude, & Latitude, as in the card of Englād following you may well perceiue. Spoudeus. Nowe I perceiue by the makinge and deſcribyng of this onely Mappe, that the whole worke doeth chieflye depende vppon the Meridian Line, appointing by them the longitudes of Regiōs : & by Paralleles of Climates, whoſe vſe in à Carde, is to limite the Latitude frō th'Equinoctiall. So that obſeruing this order of you preſcribed, I may in like forte at my pleaſure, drawe à Carde for Spaine, Fraunce, Germany, Italye, Græce, or any perticuler regiō: yea, in à warme & pleaſaunt houſe, without any perill of the raging Seas: danger of enemies: loſſe of time: ſpending of ſubſtaunce: werines of body, or anguiſhe of minde. Oh how precious â

Coſmographiceall Glaſſe. Iewell is this, it may rightly be called à Coſmographicall Glaſſe, in which we may beholde the diuerſitie of countries: natures of people, & innumerable formes of Beaſtes, Foules, Fiſhes, Trees, Frutes, Stremes, & Meatalles.   Phi.   You ſhall haue iuſt ccaſiō ſo to affirme, whan as you vnderſtande the whole cōmoditie of the ſame. But I will ſhewe you to deſcribe iij. or iiij. Regiōs in one Mappe: yea, or ſo manye as are cōteined in
the

	15	16	17	18	19	20	21	22	23	24	
61											61
60											60
59						*		Tynmouth			59
58			Kirkbie.			*					58
		Barwick.									
57			*								57
	Notinghã.		*								
56					Richmunde.						56
	Lincolne		*	*							
55					Hulle.		Tenet			55
	Yorke.		*			*					
54	Bathe.		*			*	Sandwich.				54
53			Excester.								53
			*		Bedford.	Norwich.					
52				London.		Canterburie.					52
		Portfmouth*		*							
51					Doucr. *						51
	15	16	17	18	19	20	21	22	23	24	

th'eyght portion of th'Earth.   And therefore I call it à
Carde, conteining th'eyght part of th'Earth, whose com-
                    M.j.   paſſe

paſſe, in what quãtitie you pleaſe (the greater the better)
& note, it with A.B.C for the eaſier vnderſtanding, vn
till you are exerciſed herein. Then deuide the compaſſe
of this Circle in iij equale partes, & marke the pointes of
the diuiſion, with A.B.C. After place th'one ende of the
cõpaſſe in A. & ſtretche out th'other ende vnto B. or C.
& with thy compaſſe draw an arcke, or portion of à Circle, from B. to C. Then ſet th'one ende of the compaſſe in
B. & draw the like arcke frõ A. vnto C. After place the
one ende of thy cõpaſſe in C: & deſcribe the like arck frõ
B. to A. And here note that A. doth ſignifie the North,
or ſouth Pole. And th'arke B. C. the quadrant , or iiij.
part of th'Equinoctial Circle. This arke B. C. you ſhall di
uide equallye in the middes, & at that pointe place D.
Then draw à right line from A. vnto D. this ſhall repræſent the meridiane line for the middes of this carde.
This line ſhall you diuide into 90. partes, & euery one
ſhall repræſent à digree: or into 18. portions, & euery one
ſhall anſwere vnto v. digr. Or (if the Mappe be ſmall)
into 9. portions, & euery ſuche diuiſion ſhall ſignifie. 10.
digrees. Then placing th'one ende of your compaſſe in A.
extende, or ſtretch out th'other vnto euery of theſe diui-
ſions, & drawe arkes, or portions of circles, from th'arck
A.B. vnto th'arck A.C. Theſe ended, you ſhall write in
euery diuiſion from B. to C. th'equinoctiall, vnto A. the
Pole Arctik 1. 2. 3. 4. 5. or 5. 10. 15. 20: or 10. 20. 30. according to the diuiſion of the meridiane line. After you ſhall
accompt in this diuiſion 23. digrees. 28. minutes from the
quinoctiall, which is the ſonnes greateſt declination, and

draw

draw ther à double arke whiche shall serue for the Tropicke of Cancer, or Capricorne, noted with E L, & in like manner accompt.23.degrees.28.minutes from the North or South pole, & in that space draw in like sort à double arke, which shalbe in stead of the polary circle, either Arctike or Antarctike, & set th'endes of it. I K. and so are all the paralleles of latitude, (answering your mappe) perfaitly finished.

Spou. I vnderstand the protracture of them very wel. But shall there be but one Meridiane line for all thys Mappe?

Phil. Yes verely, ther shalbe so many, as there are paralleles of latitude, whose nombre as I saide was.90.

Spou. Now I perceiue the reaso of this artificial working, for like as the circuite of the heauens is distributed into.360.parts: so in like maner the compasse of th'earth is also into 360 portions deuided, both toward the Poles & also from West to East. Therfore I pray you shew me the waye howe to draw these meridiane lines.

Philo. You shal deuide the arke B D C into.90.or.18. or els 9.portions equally, as I did the latitude from A vnto D. In like sort you shall deuide the polary Circle. I K. then drawinge in these diuisions from th'equinoctiall (by the diuisions of the Polary Circle) vnto A, Arkes or portions of Circles, you shal haue the frame preparid in whiche you shall (in the same maner that you did for England) place such portion of the world, as it can aptly receiue.

M.ij.   Spou.

Spo. But may J not deſcribe here the paralleles, & cli-
mates (taking thē out of the table in the ſecond boke) as
Ptolomæus doth in his Geographie.   *Phi. Yes verely,*
& it ſhall adorne the mappe, not omitting the principall
windes ſeruing for that part of th'earth, nor yet th'inha-
bitāts called for the diuerſitie of ſhadows, Periſcij, He-
teroſcij, Amphiſcij, but nowe beholde the frame of whoſe
compoſition we haue made ſo manye wordes.

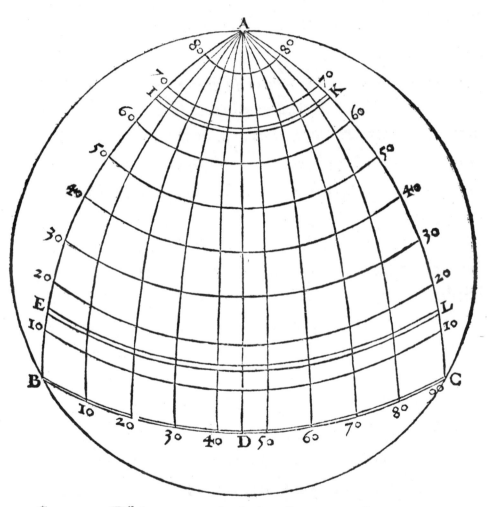

Spou.   *This mappe doth liuely expreſſe your meaning*
ſo that ther is none (I ſuppoſe) ſo ignorāt or dul, but that
without

without great difficultie he may practise the like, & ther
fore I require you procede in the descriptiõ of à Card, for
halfe the face of th'Earth whiche (as J coniecture) wyll
conueniently serue for our Hemisphere.

Philo. Not for our Hemisphere onely, but also for any
one halfe portion of th'earth, as well seruing th'vse of thẽ
that dwell vnder vs directly (& called therfore Antipodes) as also any other. But I will leaue to speake of th'vse
of it, because of it self it is manifest, & wil make plain vn
to you the cõposition, & artificial præparatiõ of it. First
with your cõpase describe à Circle as great as your carde
shalbe, withi which draw an other Circle, à finger bredth
distant, & iust to this, also an other. Then part these Cir
cles in the middes with à right lyne, th'endes of which ar
A.C. crosse this lyne in the middes, with an other ryghte
line B.D. So is your Circle parted into 4. equal portions
Then deuide euery portion in the cõpasse of the circle into 90. partes in this maner. First into 3. then euery of thẽ
againe into 3. after into 2. & laste into 5. After write in
them 5.10.15.20.25.30. &c, frõ B.C. vnto D A. & so is
the whole cõpasse of your card, parted into 360. portions.

Spoud. Vnto what vse serueth the crosse lines drawen
thorow the face of the Mappe? Philo. The line A.C.
repræsenteth the meridiane: as the line B. D. The halfe
Æquinoctiall circle. Also A.C. repræsenteth the Poles of
the world, & the plages, or partes of the same, north &
south: as B. signifieth the weast, & D. th'East.

Spou. J perceiue your minde, therfore procede. Phi.
Thẽ applie the ruler to the digr. of the circle of A.B.C

M iij,   &

& note th'interfections of the ruler in th' Æquinoctiall & in like maner do in th'other halfe Circle A.D.C. this ended, you shall defcribe from A. vnto C. Paralleles, or halfe circles, by thefe diuifions in th'Equinoctiall : then write on them from B. to D. 10 20. 30. 40. &c. Alfo you shall apply the ruler to the circle, diuiding the Meridiane line A.C. as you did th'equinoctial B.D. & defcribe in th'interfectiõs in like maner, halfe circles, which fhall ferue for Paralleles of Latitude. Then accompte in the

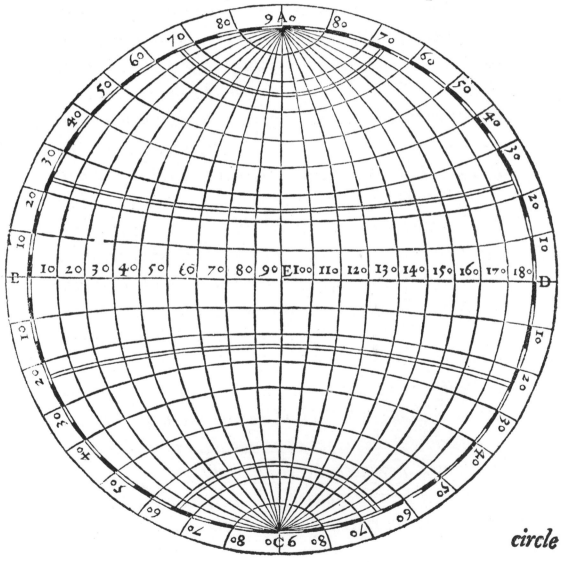

circle

circle from B.toward A.xxiij.digr.28.min. & describe an arcke, which shall repræsent the halfe tropick of Cancer, also frō A.toward B. accōpte xxiij.digr.28.min. & draw with your compasse another arcke, which shall signifie the halfe Articke, or polary circle: in like maner do with the tropike of Capricorne, & th'Antarticke circle. After place the halfe part of th'earth in the mappe thus præpared, & describe the Climates, Paralleles, inhabitaūts, & winds, with theyr proper names, & the mappe shalbe perfaitlye finished, as for example, you maye beholde the frame of the Hemisphere of th'Earth, before placed. Spou.   This carde should seme to giue à great light & knowledge vnto Nauigation. And if I do præpare me an other Mappe, for th'other Hemisphere, J shall in these two cōpræhende, & conteine th'vniuersall Earth. Phil.   Trew it is. but as touching the light, it bringeth to Nauigation, we will make mētion of, at our next meting: & now J will shewe you, how in one carde, or Mappe, you máy describe all th'earth, in such wise, as shalbe most perfait, & in that forme, & figure, whiche shalbe right pleasant. Spou.   J pray you then begin, & J shall giue diligence. Phi. First describe on some plaine place, an halfe circle A.B.C. vpō the center D. so great as thou wilte haue the carde, after deuide the right lyne A.D. into 90, portions equally. Then place th'one ende of your compasse in A. stretching forth th'other ende vnto 86. degr.xv.min. & xx, secondes, in the line A.D. & so with your Compasse, draw an arke frō D. vnto the halfe circle A.B.C. whiche shall crosse it in B, (for by

The making of a Carde conteininge the whole Earthe.

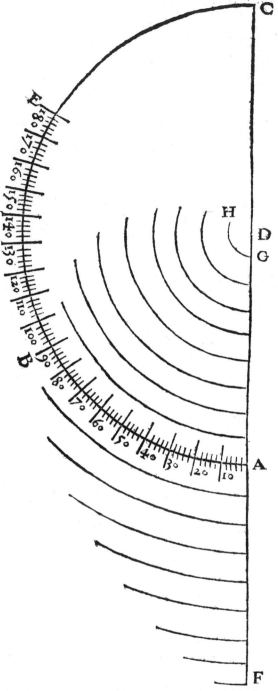

this way th'arke A. B. being extended right forth, ſhalbe as long as the right line A.D.) Then you ſhal diuide this arke A.B. into 90. equal partes. After with your compaſſe take the quãtitie of th'arke A.B. and placing th'one ende in B. take the lyke quãtitie in the half circle towardes C. whiche in like maner you ſhal diuide into 90. portiõs, & ſo th'arke A.B E ſhalbe parted into 180. parts. Again with thy compaſſe take the lengthe of the line A.D. & th'one ende beynge placed in A. take the lyke proportion from A. to F. ſo that A.F. ſhalbe e-quall to the line A.D. Then diuide the line A.F. into 90. partes equally, as you did A.D. after placing th'one

of

fote of thy cōpaſſe in the Cēter D.thou ſhalt draw arkes
in euery of the diuiſiōs,or els euery fift,or x.diuiſion onlye & note the hieſt Arke nexte with G.H.then enter
into the table folowing,&find out how many degrees in
lōgitude anſwereth to.80.degrees of latitude,north frō
th'equinoctiall(which in the table are.140.degrees.40
minutes) that number you ſhal accompt in the half circle from A,vnto E.& applying your ruler vnto th'end
of this nōber,& vnto the cēter D.draw à ſhort line,whi-
che ſhal extēd vnto H. again enter into your table with
70.degrees of Latitude , & you ſhall finde.138.degrees
23.minutes(which f accompt from A,toward E as before,& applying my ruler to the ſhorte line , & the degrees in Lōgitude,with my pen f draw an other ſhorte
line.In like maner f do with th'other paralleles of La-
titude.60.50.40.30.20.10. Spou. So that by entringe
into the table,& accompting the degrees in Longitude
frō A. towardes E,& drawing ſhort lines one at th'end
of an other,ther ariſeth as it wer a portion of a circle frō
D to B.& if I could in like maner find the proportiō of
th'equinoctiall vnto the South paralleles (whiche in like
nōbre are.90.)thē the whole forme wolde repraeſent the
figure of half an hart. Phi. Th'other parte of the Table conteining Southe paralleles ,ſhall ſerue herein your
vſe ſufficiētly.For entring into it with.x.degrees of latitude which is the next ſouth parallele frō th'equinoctial,
f find.79.degrees.46.min.which accompting as before
in the halfe circle AE.f drawe an other ſhorte line at
th'end of th'other,& ſo in like ſorte with.20.30.40.50.

60

A TABLE, CONTENING THE SEGMENTES

and partes of th'equinoctiall, drawne in a plaine plat forme, answering vnto the circumference of Paralleles. &c.

The North Latitude of Paralleles							Paralleles drawn South frō th'Equinoctial					
Di	Dig	M.	Di	Dig	40		Di.	Di	Mi	Di	Di	Miunt.
89	141	20	44	126	40		1	88	59	46	41	22
88	141	20	43	126	2		2	87	59	47	40	19
87	141	19	42	125	22		3	86	58	48	39	16
86	141	16	41	124	44		4	85	59	49	38	12
85	141	12	40	124	4		5	84	53	50	37	8
84	141	7	39	123	16		6	83	55	51	36	4
83	141	1	38	122	44		7	82	52	52	35	0
82	140	55	37	122	4		8	81	51	53	33	56
81	140	47	36	121	20		9	80	17	54	32	53
80	140	40	35	120	38		10	79	46	55	32	2
79	140	27	34	119	55		11	78	44	56	31	2
78	140	22	33	119	10		12	77	41	57	30	0
77	140	4	32	118	55		13	76	38	58	29	0
76	139	58	31	117	41		14	75	33	59	28	5
75	139	46	30	116	58		15	74	31	60	27	0
74	139	30	29	116	9		16	73	27	61	26	1
73	139	14	28	115	21		17	72	25	62	25	2
72	138	45	27	114	33		18	71	19	63	24	2
71	138	38	26	113	45		19	70	16	64	23	3
70	138	23	25	112	56		20	69	12	65	22	5
69	138	13	24	112	6		21	68	7	66	21	6
68	137	56	23	111	17		22	67	3	67	20	9
67	137	32	22	100	27		23	65	50	68	19	12
66	137	15	21	109	35		24	64	55	69	18	16
65	136	55	20	108	55		25	63	50	70	17	20
64	136	33	19	107	52		26	62	45	71	16	23
63	136	10	18	106	58		27	61	40	72	15	27
62	135	47	17	106	9		28	60	36	73	14	31
61	135	25	16	105	13		29	59	32	74	13	37
60	135	0	15	104	19		30	58	41	75	12	43
59	134	35	14	103	22		31	57	23	76	11	49
58	134	6	13	102	29		32	56	18	77	10	55
57	133	41	12	101	34		33	55	13	78	10	1
56	133	12	11	100	39		34	54	8	79	9	8
55	132	43	10	99	42		35	53	5	80	8	17
54	132	15	9	98	45		36	52	0	81	7	26
53	131	48	8	97	49		37	50	55	82	6	35
52	131	16	7	96	51		38	49	51	83	5	44
51	130	44	6	95	53		39	48	44	84	4	55
50	130	10	5	94	52		40	47	43	85	4	2
49	129	37	4	93	58		41	46	39	86	3	13
48	129	2	3	92	58		42	45	34	87	2	24
47	128	29	2	91	58		43	44	31	88	1	35
46	127	52	1	91	0		44	43	28	89	0	47
45	127	16	0	90	0		45	42	25	90	0	0

60.70.80.90.*where the Pole Antarctike is, and ma-*
keth the Figure as you faid of halfe an hart.

Spoud.   *This can I practife by my felfe at an other*
feafon:wherefore I praye you procede to the finifhinge of
this Mappe.

Philo.   *Then takinge the Clothe or Parchemente,*
in whiche you will defcribe the Paralleles, and Meri-
diane Circles:you fhall reduce all the Circles with theyr
diuifions,whiche you made in A.B.C.into this feconde
Mappe, the Center of whiche is.K.by the healpe of
your compaffe ,firfte drawinge a righte line.K.L. the
middes of whiche fhall be M.and this line mufte be
in lengthe equall to the Line.D.F.in the firft Mappe.
Then placinge th'one ende of the compaffe in.K.ex-
tende th'other vnto.M.and protracte a Circle,whi-
che fhall reprefente th'Equinoctiall,and fhall be equall
vnto the Circle.A.B.C after take with your Com-
paffe the diftaunce of euerye Arcke defcribed in the
firfte Mappe,and wyth th'one fote of your compaffe,
(placinge th'other foote in.K.)drawe Cyrcles in fuche
circuit,as one of thefe fhalbe foure times the quantity of
one of th'other in the firfte Mappe.

Moreouer you fhall diuide th'Equinoctiall line in-
to.360.equall portions ,fuche as are in the Line.A.
B.C.In like forte th'other Paralleles,bothe Septemtri-
onall,and Southe from th'Equinoctiall , and drawinge
from euerye diuifion of one Parallele vnto an other fhort
lynes as you did from.D.to.H. in the firfte Mappe,
                                                    your

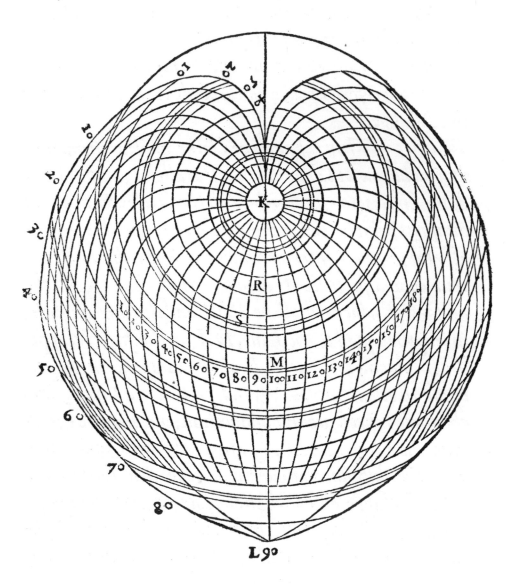

*your Carde will not onlye growe to the forme of a harte,
but also of a double herte one within an other , as thys
demonstratiõ, & figure sheweth. Last you shal drawe the
Tropickes of Cancer and Capricorny, the Circles Arcticke and Antarctike, makinge them double lines for the
easier knowinge them from th'other paralleles.*

Then

Then place in thys Mappe the Face of th'Earthe, accordinge to his partes in Longitude and Latitude, as it
is set fourth in my fifth booke, vsinge in euery Countrye,
to place onlye the Meridiane Line, for the middes of
the same, where as your Mappe is of no greate quantitye. Then place the degrees of Longitude, & Latitude
vnto the Paralleles, and Meridiane Circles, with Climates, Windes, diuersity of inhabitaunce, and other necessarye thynges.

Spoud. But maye I not describe the Planet & signe
vnder whiche euerye nation is, also in this Mappe? for
Ptolomæus maketh mention of them in his quadripar-
tite, as also euery Astronomer wryting of the reuolutiōs
of the world. Phi. Yes truely, & by that reason, you
shall make it an Astronomical Glasse also, & serue your
vse profitablye therein. Spoud. I praye you geue me
a table of the principall windes, of whiche you haue hetherto made no mention, & also of the Planets & signes, vnder whome euery region & Country is gouerned.
Phi. As touchinge the windes, and there nombre, because it requireth a longer time then now is offered, you
shall finde in the table of thē where we make mention of
Nauigatiō: but as for the Planets & signes gouerning
euery region, because you haue not alway Ptolomæus, I
will not refuse to make mentiō of it in this place, adding
furdermore vnto Ptolomæus the names both of Regions, and Cities, which ether were not knowne of hym, or
els willingly omitted. As in this Table you maye easelye
perceiue, cōferrīg it with that which is of him described.

N.i.

Regi-

Regions and Cities, subiect to the signes & Planets, and first of those that be vnder Aries, and Mars.

V.♂

Basternia, Syria, Palestina, England, Fraunce, Germany, Burgundie, Sweueland: and of Cities wyth Townes, Naples, Ancona, Ferrariæ, Florens, Verona Capua, Lindauia, Cracouia. &c.

♉.♀

Vnder Taurus, and Venus.

Parthia, Media, Cyprus, the lesser Asia, th'Ilandes named Cyclades, Irelande, Heluetia. &c. Of Cities and townes, Bonony, Tigure, Lucerna, Herbipolis, Lipsia, Posna. &c.

♊.☿

Vnder Gemini, and Mercurius.

Hircania, Armenia, Cyrene, Marmarica, the lower Ægipt, à part of Lombardie and Fläders, Brabant: and of Cities and Townes, London, Louain, Brigys, Mence, Hasford, Norinberge. &c.

♋.☽

Vnder Cancer, and the Mone.

Numidia, Africa, Bithynia, Carthage, Phrigia, Hollande, Seland, Scotland, the kingdome of Granat. &c: And of Cities & Townes, Constantinople, Venice, pise, Millan, Treuers, York, S.Andrews, Lubeck.

Vnder Leo, and the sonne.

♌.☉

Italy, Sicilie Apulie, Boheme, Phænicia, à part of Turkie, Sabina. &c. And of Cities with townes, Damascus. Rome, Confluence, Rauenna, Cremona. Prage.

Vnder Virgo, and Mercurius.

♍.☿

Mesopotamia, Babilon, Assiria, Grece, Achaia Crete: and of Cities and of townes, Hierusalē, Corinth, the

Rhodes, Papia, Tolose, Lions, Paryce, Heydelberge, Basile.   Vnder Libra, & Venus.   ♎.♀

Bactriana, Caspia, Thebaida, Æthiopia, Lyuonia, Austrige, Oasis. And of cities & towns, Caïeta, Lauda, Suessa, Placentia, Friburge, Argentine, Spiers, Francford. &c.   Vnder Scorpius and Mars.   ♏.♂

Iudæa, Cappadocia, Getulia, Mauritania, Norway, Cathalonia. And of Cities and Townes, Valentia, Padua, Messana, Aquileia. &c.
Under Sagittarius, & Iubiter   ♐.♃

Spayne, Arabia the happy, Ungary, Slauonia, Celtica, Misnia. And of Cities & Townes, Tolet, Collein, Narbona, Stutgardia, Rotenburge, Buda. &c.
Vnder Capricornus, & Saturnus.   ♑.♄

India, Arriana, Macedonia, Thracia, Grece, Saxonye, Hessia, Orchney Flands, Machline, Oxford, Brädenburge, Constantia, Fauentia. Augusta vindel. &c.
Under Aquarius, & Saturne.   ♒.♄

Arabie desert, great Tartarie, Denmark, Segdiana, Sarmatia. & of Cities, Hamburge, Brema, Salisburge. &c.   Under Pisces & Iubiter.

Lydia, Paphylia, Calabria, Normandy, Portugal Sicilie. & of cities & townes, Alexäder. Hispalis, Copostel, Ratisbone, Worms. Sp. Ther now remaineth to speke of the describing à perticuler card for any regiö or coütry, without knowinge their lögitudes & latitudes. Ph. That is well remëbred, & ther be diuers, & sodri waies to performe this work, of which I wil shew you but one: that is by an instrumët, seruing properly to this vse.   ♓.♃

But like as this waie is more easier then that whiche is
performed by longitude, & Latitude, & may be put in
practice at all times: so in like condition, the worcke is
not so exacte, and perfaite, as by Longitudes and Latitudes, whiche require longe and diligent obseruation.
Spou. In what form is th'instrumēt made by which so
much vtilitie may spring, as to describe by it, a country.
Philonicus.   It is made muche like the backe parte
of an Astrolabe, conteininge in the circuite. 360. de-

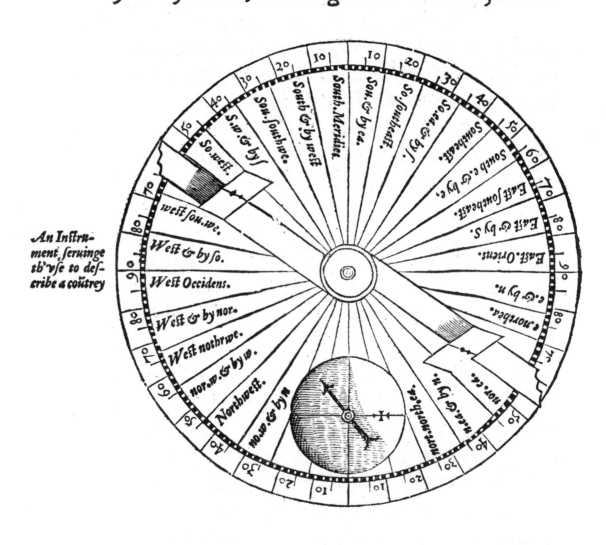

*An Instru-
ment seruinge
th'vse to des-
cribe a coūtrey*

grees

grees , and hathe à ruler with two sightes , whiche we moue to and fro, as occasion is ministred , vntill thorowe them we see the place desired. But it differeth from an Astrolabe, in that it hath à Diall, with à Nedle fixed in it, & also that th'Instrument is diuided into two & thirtie partes, like as à Shipmans compasse. As this figure before placed, doth apparantly set out.

Spoudeus.   This Instrument is easye to be prouided, yea, & that without great expence, & is not troublous in cariage: but in what sorte may I by it describe à Country?

To make à Carte without knowing Lögitude, & Latitude.

Philon.   I will in fewe wordes make it to you euident. With youre Instrumente you shall ascende on some hie towre, Steaple, or Mountayne, so that you may on euery part se the townes, & Villagies, aboute you adiacent in your Horizont. Then placing your Instrument (which I name à Geographicall plaine Sphere) Flat, & leuell, tourninge it from one parte vnto an other, vntil the nedle fall on the Meridian Line , in thy Geographicall plaine Spheare, then it remaininge stedfaste: directe the ruler with hys two sightes vnto anye one place that you do see, & marke diligently th'Angle of sight, (Gemma Frisius calleth it) Angulus positionis.

The Geographicall plaine Sphere.

Th'Angle of sight.

Spoude.   I praye you be not offended althoughe at thys presente I interrupte you, and or you further procede shewe me what you call the Angle of sight.

Philonicus.   I am nothynge displeased , but muche reioyse that you will not negligentlye suffer

N iij.   thinges

thinges to escape you, vntill you be satisfied touchinge
their true meaninge. You shall note that the Angle of

Th' Angle of sight. sighte, is that Arke or portion of the Horizont of anye
place, comprehended betwixte two Meridiane Circles
and drawne by the verticall Circle of the first place, vnto the Meridian of the secõde, whose distaunce you seke

A perfit An-gle. out.   Spou.   Then you in this place call that Arke
of the Horizont, the Angle of sighte, whiche is lesser
then à perfait angle, conteininge.90.degrees.

Phil.   I do so, for if it be.90.degrees, the place is vnder the same Parallele of Latitude, but yet differeth in
Longitude, & therefore is directly East or West, as also
if there be no Angle of sighte, it hathe the same Longitude & meridiane Line, & is plaine North or South
from you.

Spoud.   Then I pray you proceade with your precept,
you saye I shall take the Angles of sight of euerye place
that I can see in the Horizont of my place where I begin my worke.

Phil.   Yea verelye, and then you shall make in some
Paper à greate Circle, & deuide it into.360.partes, as
your Geographicall plaine Sphere is, writinge the foure
coastes of the countrey East, South, West, & North, in
your paper, then draw right lines frõ the Center of your
circle, (whiche representeth your place where you take
th' Angles of sight of other townes, & villagies adiacẽt)
vnto suche Angles of sighte as you haue founde oute by
your Geographicall plain Sphere.

Spou.   But this shall litle (as I cõiecture) auayle: yea
al-

althoughe I might haue th' Angles of sight of all the places in a Regiõ, from my place, if I haue not the trewe
distaunce of them?

Philon.   I cõfesse no lesse: for if you haue not th' Angles of sighte from ij. places, you can not gather the distaunce of the thirde. Therfore when as you haue placed
in the Paper all the Townes, Villages, or notable hils,
that you can se in that Horizont: you shall take your instrument and Paper, trauelinge vnto some other town,
where in like manner you shall go vp into the hiest place
of the same, and there placinge your instrumente as before, obserue th' Angles of sight of such Townes & Villagies as are in that Horizont. Whiche ended, you shall
describe in the Paper an other circle as before (as farre
distaunte frõ th'other, as you thinke conueniente, marking diligentlye that the Center of the second Circle, be
in the line of sighte, drawne from the Center of the firste
Circle, it beinge also deuided into. 360. partes) drawing
such Angles of sight as you can finde. And so procede frõ
place to place, vntil euery Towne or Village haue come
twise in your sight. And where that anye line of the seconde Circle, Crosseth the like line in the firste Circle,
make there a Sterre, or like marke, for that thirde place
(so call I the towne obserued twise) & so in like manner you shall do with other places, vntil you haue drawn
the hole region you desire.

Spoud.   Than it is expediente for me to obserue the
Angle of sighte of euerye Towne, from ij. seueral places,
so shall I finde oute the distaunce of one of them from an

N.iiij.   other,

other, or of the thirde frō thē both, as it muſt be placed in the Card. Phil. Yea, and not only in the Card, but that being knowen, you ſhall eaſely finde out the diſtaunce in miles of one of them from an other.

Spou.   That ſemeth very meruelous, ſeyng that you haue not theyr Longitudes & Latitudes.

Phil,   Yet the worke is right eaſie) as I doubte not but you will confeſſe) for knowing the diſtaunce in miles of anye Townes, or Villagies, you ſhall knowe the true diſtaunce of all the Townes in an Region, one from an other, as for example.

Swarſton in Norfolk, is from Norwich. iij. miles: I deuide as you ſe the line drawne from Norwiche to it with my compaſſe, in three equall parts, & after applye my compaſſe to the line drawne frō Norwich to Windham, & from Windham to Swarſton, & find. vi. miles betwixt Norwich and Windham, and. iiij miles from Windā to Swarſton. Spo.   By this way, I can finde

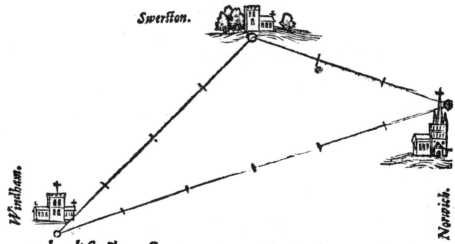

out the diſtaūce of two townes nie together, & by that to finde out the diſtaūce of all townes in à Carde.

Philo.

Phi. *I do greatly commend you, and you may also make a scale, or ruler, conteininge in it the quantitye of miles from one, to an hundreth if you please, and by this menes you may take with your compasse the distance of ij. pla- ces, & then apply the compasse to the foresaide scale, or ruler, & you shall finde the perfaite distance. And nowe sence I haue fulfilled your mind for the chief & princi- pall matters belóging to Cosmographie, & Geographie, I will at this present returne to my lodginge againe.*

Howe to finde the distaunce of places.

Spou. *Whan shall it be your pleasure, that I shall re- paire vnto you to be instructed in the Terestriall Globe, because you saide that it do mooste aptlye represente the forme of th'Earthe.*

Philo. *Being required by certain of my frendes, I do entend, to make a longer & more ample discourse ther- in, then this place will permit: And therfore will at thys time omit it. As touching my fift booke you shall receiue it of me to morrow, which day also for your furderaunce, I entende to consume in teaching you necessarye principles for Hydrographie and Nauiga- tion. And therefore agayne*
• fare you well.

THE FOVRTH BOOKE OF

the Cosmographicall Glasse, setting out such necessary
principles, & rules, as are to be obserued in
Hydrographie, & Nauigation.

Spoudæus.

Time tedious.

THERE IS NO-thing vnder the Globe of the mone conteined, whiche vnto man, beast & e-uerye liuinge wite, semeth more tedious, more icke-some, and long the time, when as they once fele the wante of that they moste desire. Whiche sayinge to be true (althoughe manye do confesse) yet I aboue all other muste of force affirme, re-membringe your promesse, touchinge th' Arte of Na-uigation. For sence your departure, the greadye Grey-hounde (I assure you) neuer more desired his pray, nor the thirstye harte, the flowynge fountaine, or the langui-shinge sicke paciente, the recouery of his health: then my minde wanting her fode and Nutrimente, thoughte longe, wished, and thirsted, after youre presence and companye.

Phi. It is the proper nature of suche in whose mynde knoweledge haue once builded her Boure, euer more & more (like à couetous mã) to labour & trauell after
science

ſciēce: for ther is no other waies, how to expel that foule,
& vglie beaſt Ignorance, out of the minde of mã : & to
place knowledge in the ſame, but by all poſſible meanes,
to imbrace Sciēce & Cunning. Wherfore, leſt that your
paine ſhould with Tantalus increaſe: I wil no lenger oc-
cupie the time with other kinde of talke , but will begin
ſomwhat tointreat of neceſſary thinges belōging to Na
uigatiō: for I do not intende to ſet out the differēs of one
veſſell frō an other, as th'Argouſie, Hulke, Ship, Craer,
Pincke, Pynice, Gally, or what ſo euer name they haue,
nor yet of theyr takling: but wil leaue it to ſuch as are Pi
lotes & maſters of that facultie, & will ſhew thē à way
how they ſhall both correcte their errours, & alſo guide
& direct their Veſſels, accordiug t'Arte & Science.
Spo.   Thē firſt I pray you begin with the diuiſiō of the
water, expoūding ſuch names as they take of ther place.
Phi. That was my meaning: & firſt as touching the ſeas
you ſhal note that it is diuerſly called: either according to
the hole, or els accordig to the part. Accordig to the hole,
as the ſeas by this generall name Oceã, becauſe they circuit th'earth roūde about. according to the partes, as the
ſeas breaking into the land, & making bāckes on either
ſide is called Sinus, takinge alſo the name of the place it
floweth into, as Sinus Adriaticus , ſinus Arabicus , Sinus Indicus & c. Alſo the great ſeas which diuideth Afrik
& Europe, is called the midle erth ſea: taking that name
becauſe in the Weaſt of Spaine , it breaketh into the
middes of th'Earth. The Redde ſeas where proud Pha-
ro & all his bende were drenched : is not farre diſtante
                                                from

Th'Ocean ſea

*Sinus, what it
here ſignifieth*

*Mare mediter
ranium.*

The red Seas.

Mare Mortu-um.

from the midde Earthe Seas, for there is but à certayne hyll, whiche they muſt nedes go ouer that go by land frō Egipte to Arabia Petrea, that parketh them. Alſo the Sodomiticall or dead Seas (ſo called becauſe that Sodōe & other Cities were there burnt with fire coming from heauen) is not farre from Iordane, it is alſo called the dead ſea, becauſe the water moueth not, no not with moſt vehement tempeſtes, becauſe of the pitch in it, nether cā any ſhippe ſaile, or any fiſhe liue there. The ſeas whyche are vnder the Poles Arcticke & Antarcticke are called

Mare Cogela-tum.

the congeled or froſen Seas. There are alſo the Engliſh, Germaine, Spaniſhe & other ſeas, of whiche I neade to make no mention, no more then of the notable riuers, as the Themes, the Rhine, Ganges, Neccarus, Danu-bie, Tyber, Nilus. &c. Becauſe they are manifeſt vn-to ſuche as trauell in any of them.

Spoud.   I read alſo in diuerſe writers theſe wordes, Fretum, Lacus, Stagnum, Palus, Fluuius. But theyr difference I know not.

What Fretum is.

Phil. Fretum is cōtrary to that peaſe of th'Earth, that is called Iſthmus. For like as that is à ſtreight portion of th'Earth, hauinge the Seas on bothe ſides: ſo Fretum is à narrowe & ſtreit arme of the Seas, beyng betwixte two

What Lacus is.

What Stag-num is.

ſhores. Lacus, & we may call it à lake, is that which cō-tinually hath water. Stagnum do differ from it, becauſe it conteyneth only water gathered by inundations, and

What Palus is

raine in the winter ſeaſon. Palus is à water merueilus deape, & broade, & Fluius, we name it à fludde, & is called ſo of flowyng.

Spou.

Spoud. *Your wordes giueth me occation to demaunde the cause of ebbing, & flowing, & also whether the time may by any meane be learned?*

Philon. *And I will gladly answere you, for this is not the least thing that Pilotes, & Shipmen ought to haue regarde vnto, bothe for goyng out, & also comminge in into any Porte, or Hauen, & other necessarye matters. & as touchinge the Seas howe that they raise, and Eleuate vp them selues, as though they would touch the firmament, and there with filleth other Armes, Hauens, and waters: and also, that they waxe shallowe, and as it were emptye againe: I can coniecture no other cause then that, which the Noble Philosopher & Phisitian Galenus citith, in his boke De diebus decretorijs: in which he affirmeth that whē as the Mone increse in light, al moist thinges in like case increase: & when as her light decreaseth, they in like sort decrease. Wherby it is euident that spring, & ebbe tides, take their beginning & end of the mones course in the Zodiack. Galenus words are these.*

The cause of spring & ebbe tides.

Πάντα μὲν γὰρ ἅ δρᾶν πέφυκεν, ἀμυδρα γινεται μηνοειδῦς γενομένης ἀυτης, ἅπαντα δὲ ἰσχυρα πεπληρωμένης.

Li.3.de Dieb. decret.cap.2.

Omnia siquidem quæ facere nata est, vbi falcis figurā repræfentat languida fiunt: inualefcunt omnia cum plena fuerit.

All thinges which are vnder the power of the Moone, when as she refembleth the fith in likenes, they are feble, & decrease: but al thinges waxe & increase, when she is at the Full.

Spou. *Then by these wordes I gather à repugnancie betwixt his authoritie, & dayly experience: for it is more manifest, & clere thē midday, how that the seas ebbe, & flow euery natural day, that is in 24. houres*

An obiection.

twise: & Galenus saith, how but twise in à Month the Seas ebbe & flow: for because she is but once at the full, & once at the chaunge in this circuit of time.

Th'answere. Phi. This obiection nothing infringeth Galen his authoritie, nor yet experience. For in the spring, and ebbe tides, the seas do encrease, & decrese meruelously: whiche happen but twise euery mōth, & this is that, which Galen ment. And as for daily ebbing, & flowinge, the seas do not increase, or decrease therwith. And therfore is properlye called fluxus, et refluxus, but th'other *Augmentum et Decrementum maris.*

Spo. And what is the cause of this dailye ebbinge and flowinge so orderlye, as often & sundrye times J haue well noted?

The cause of Ebbyng and flowing. Phi. The mone also, for when as she riseth in th'East, the seas begin to increase more & more, vntill she commeth to the Meridian Circle, & is full Southe: & then causeth full Sea. And so as she declineth from the South, so the sea decrease, vntill she go downe in the Weast Ocean, at whiche time againe the Seas begin to increase, vntill the Moone be in the foresaide Meridian Line, vnder th'earth, & then she is full North, making also full seas. So they decrease by little & little as the Mone aprocheth toward th'East.

Spou. Then I praye you teache me some briefe waye how I maye at all times finde th'age of the Mone withoute anye tables of her diurnall course, or Ephemerides: for hauing that, J shall easlye finde oute the springe and ebbe tides.

Philo-

Philon. *With à right good will, you shall accompt the daies, that are past of thy month, & adde thereto the E-pacte, And to this number you shall also adde for euerye month past (beginning at Marche) 1. These 3, numbers you shall adde together, and that shall shew you the age of the Mone. As for example 1559, the 24. daye of August, J wolde knowe the mones age. Firste I adde 24 daies to th'Epact which is 22, the number of them is 46, then from March to August, ther are 5. Monthes past, therfore I adde to 46. the number of 5. and the hole number is fiftie one, from whiche J take thirtie, (for so must you do, if your number be more then xxx. & vnder sixtie) & there remaine, one & twentie, which is th'age of the Mone.*

Spoud. *And what if the number be 30. or 60. what must J then do?*

Philonicus. *There is no thing to do, for that number sheweth the Moone to chaunge that presente daye.*

Spoude. *And howe may I finde the trewe Epacte, for on that is all the difficulte of the worke?*

Philon. *That is so easie, as I counte it but lost time to make many wordes there in. For hauinge th'Epacte for one yeare: you shal for the next yeare adde xi. & so yerelie xi. & cast awaye xxx. as ofte as you can: & the remnent, shalbe youre Epacte. But because I will not make more wordes in trifles, beholde the Table, and whan the yeares are expired, begin againe at the firste numbre, & so continew for euer without variation.*

The yere of Chrift	The gol dē num.	Th'E pacte	The yere of Chrift	The gol dē num	Th'E pacte
1560	3	3	1570	13	23
1561	4	14	1570	14	4
1562	5	25	1572	15	15
1563	6	6	1573	16	26
1564	7	17	1574	17	7
1565	8	28	1575	18	18
1566	9	9	1576	19	29
1567	10	20	1577	1	11
1568	11	1	1578	2	22
1569	12	12			

Spou.   *Nowe if I coulde know, howe long the Moone doth euery night ſhine, me thinke it ſhould be very pleaſaunt & comfortable, eſpecially beyng on the troublous ſeas.*   Philoni.   *And to that thinge alſo, you ſhall eaſely attaine by the helpe of the Table folowing.*

A TABLE OF THE SONNE RISINGE
and going downe, throughe the whole yeare.

Da. of the mō	Ianuarius. Sonne rise.	Sonne go do.	Februarius. Sonne rise.	Sonne go do.	Martius. Sonne rise.	Sonne go do.	Aprill. Sonne rise.	Sonne go do.	Maye. Sonne rise.	Sonne go do.	Iune. Sonne rise.	Sonne go do.
	H M	H M	H M	H M	H M	H M	H M	H M	H M	H M	H M	H M
1	7 47	4 13	7 5	4 55	6 16	5 44	5 23	6 37	4 36	7 24	4 7	7 53
5	7 42	4 18	6 59	5 1	6 9	5 51	5 16	6 44	4 31	7 29	4 5	7 55
10	7 36	4 24	6 50	5 10	6 0	6 0	5 8	6 52	4 25	7 35	4 4	7 56
15	7 30	4 30	6 42	5 18	5 51	6 9	5 0	7 0	4 19	7 41	4 4	7 56
20	7 24	4 26	6 34	5 26	5 42	6 18	4 51	7 9	4 14	7 46	4 6	7 54
25	7 17	4 43	6 24	5 36	5 34	6 26	4 43	7 17	4 11	7 49	4 9	7 51

Da. of the mō	Iulius. Sonne rise.	Sonne go do.	Auguſt. Sonne rise.	Sonne go do.	September. Sonne rise.	Sonne go do.	Octuber. Sonne rise.	Sonne go do.	Nouember. Sonne rise.	Sonne go do.	December. Sonne rise.	Sonne go do.
	H M	H M	H M	H M	H M	H M	H M	H M	H M	H M	H M	H M
1	4 12	7 48	4 48	7 12	5 39	6 21	6 32	5 28	7 22	4 38	7 53	4 7
5	4 15	7 45	4 55	7 5	5 46	6 14	6 39	5 21	7 28	4 32	7 55	4 5
10	4 20	7 49	5 3	6 57	5 54	6 6	6 47	5 13	7 34	4 26	7 56	4 4
15	4 26	7 34	5 11	6 49	6 4	5 56	6 55	5 5	7 40	4 20	7 55	4 5
20	4 32	7 28	5 18	6 42	6 13	5 47	7 4	4 56	7 45	4 15	7 54	4 6
25	4 38	7 22	5 26	6 34	6 21	5 39	7 12	4 48	7 49	4 11	7 51	4 9

Firſt

First you shall seke out the Monthe in this table, with
his day, which if it be not there expressed, take that whiche is next it. And it shall shewe you what time the sonne
setteth: after, seke out th'age of the Mone by th'Epacte,
or otherwise, & againſt that number in this table (intituled the time that the mone shineth. &c.) You shal find
houres, & minutes, which adde to the going down of the
sonne, & that nomber shall manifeſtly declare how long
she is aboue th'Earthe, as for example. The. xx. daye of
Marche. 1559. the Mone is xj. daies olde: againſt which
number in the Table of hyr shining, I finde viij. houres,
48. minutes. Thē do I loke at what tyme the sonne setteth the. xx. day of March, & find it at vi. of the clocke
xviij. minutes. Theſe I adde together, and the numbre
is xv. hours vi. minutes : so that the mone sheweth vnto
iii. of the clocke in the morning, & vi. minutes after. &
heare you muſte note, that before the Full, & after the
chaunge, she shineth preſently, the sonne beinge set. But
after the Full mone, you shall subtract oute of the sonnes
rising, so many hours & minuts, as you finde in th'age of
the mone: & the remanent, shal shew when as she do riſe
as for example. The xxvij. day of March, the moone is
xviij. daies old, the time of hir shining, is x. houres xxiiij
minutes: the sonne riſeth that day, at v. of the clock. xxx
minutes. Now subtract the shining of the Mone, out
of the sonnes rising: there remaine vii. houres vi. minuts,
the time whan as the Mone shall shew her selfe aboue
the Horizont.

To know howe
lōg the Moone
doth shine eue-
ry night.

An example.

An example.

O.iij.　　　　The

A TABLE SHEVVING HOVVE LONG
the Moone shineth in our Horizont.

Th'age of the Mone.	The time she shineth.		Th'age of the Mone.	The time she shineth.	
Dayes.	Hovr.	Min.	Dayes.	Hour.	Min.
1	0	48	16	12	0
2	1	36	17	11	12
3	2	24	18	10	24
4	3	12	19	9	36
5	4	0	20	8	48
6	4	48	21	8	0
7	5	36	22	7	12
8	6	24	23	6	24
9	7	12	24	5	36
10	8	0	25	4	48
11	8	48	26	4	0
12	9	36	27	3	12
13	10	24	28	2	24
14	11	12	29	1	36
15	12	0	30	0	48

Spoudæus. *There yet remain to set out, at what time daily ebbing and flowing shalbe in euery cost or you furder proceade : for you haue declared the diuision of the seas : with the cause of the springe and ebbe tides, also of dailye ebbinge, and flowinge, moreouer, the age of the Mone, and how long she shineth, wherby I can coniecture the tides aforesaid: nowe therfore if you do instructe me, wherby I may know the perfect time of Ebbinge and Flowinge: then you maye with other thynges at your pleasure proceade.*

Philon. *That you may do without any labour or studye, if you do, but only know what Mone in that coaste make ful seas: which thinge this Table folowynge shall leade you vnto, in which, I haue placed the principall townes on this shore of England, & of other costes, with the Mone that in euerye one of them make full seas.*

Full

FVLL SEAS IN THESE PLACES FO-
lowynge by the coste of the Moone, as whan she is at

London.	S.VV.	Al the coast à long, till you come	
Graues ende.	S.VV.S.	to Poell head S.w. From Po=	
Poperelle.	S.	ell head til you come to the streit	
Landes ende.	S.E.	of Malgate.S.w.	
Marget.	S.S.E.	Grauelin	S.E.
Gulles.	S.VV	Dunkerk	S.E.
Sandwich	S.E.S.	Hoste Ende.	S.S.w.
Douer.	S.E.S.	Blanke Borow.	S.S.w.
Rhie.	S.S.E.	Sluse.	S.ſ.w.
Porchmouth.	S.	Ramkinse	ſ.ſ.w.
Portland.	S.E.	At Anwerpe.	E.
Dartmot	VV.S.	Newporte	ſ.ſ.w.
Plumot	VV.S.	Harwich	ſ.ſ.E.
Famot.	VV.S.	Yermouth	ſ.E.
Mous bay.	VV.	All the coast à longe to VVin=	
Scilli.	VV.S.	tertone.	ſ.E.
Milford.	VV.S.	Humber.	E.
The lands end at Gulf.VV.S.VV		Scarborow, and à longe the	
And all the coastes vp to bristow,		coast to Newcastell.	ſ.w.
yea and the coastes of Irlande, frō		Castell.	ſ.ſ.w.
VVaterforde, vnto Holdhēde of		Holly Ilande.	ſ.ſ.w.
Kinſſael.	w.S.	Barwike	ſ.ſ.w.
Calys.	S.S.E.	South Hāpton.	S.
Boleyne.	S.S.E.	Blacke Deppes	S.
Depe.	S.E.S.	Redde Bancke.	S.
New Hauen	S.E.S.	Tyne Mouth.	ſ.w.
The coast of Lions.S.ſ.w.		Hartle Poule.	w.S.w.
Conquit.	S.w.	Feylene.	VV.S.

Spo. This I vnderstande very well.

Phi. Then when you will learne the time that it shall
be full sea, seke out the towne with the coast of the mone.
After, enter into this table (hauiug th'age of the mone)
& there stay your finger. Then seke in the hier or lower
part of the Table, for suche a coast as you founde writen

How to know th'exacte time of ebbinge and flowyng.

To the Reader.

Heare should come into this Page (frendly Reader) the table of the Mones ebbinge and flowinge : but because the space is not sufficient, you shall finde it, in an open sheet, whiche must here to be annexid.

with

A PROFITABE TABLE FOR FINDINGE OVT EBBES, AND FLVDDES IN THE COASTES
of Englande, Scotlande, Irelande, Duchelande, and Fraunce.

THE COATSES OF THE MOONE BEFORE
the Full, & after the Chaunge.

Th'age of the Mone	East.	East & by S.	East. S.E.	S.e. & by Ea.	S.Ea.	S.E. & by So.	S.S. Eaft.	S. and by Ea.	Sou,	S. and by we.	S.S. weaft	S.we. & by f	S.we.	f.w. & by w.	we.S. weaft	we. & by So.
1	6 48	7 33	8 18	9 3	9 48	10 33	11 18	12 1	12 48	1 31	2 18	3 3	3 48	4 33	5 18	6 3
2	7 36	8 21	9 6	9 51	10 36	11 21	12 6	12 51	1 36	2 21	3 6	3 51	4 36	5 21	6 6	6 51
3	8 24	9 9	9 54	10 30	11 24	12 9	12 54	1 39	2 24	3 9	3 54	4 39	5 24	6 9	6 54	7 39
4	9 12	9 57	10 42	11 27	12 12	12 57	1 42	2 27	3 12	3 57	4 42	5 27	6 12	6 57	7 42	8 27
5	10 0	10 45	11 30	12 15	1 0	1 45	2 30	3 15	4 0	4 45	5 30	6 15	7 0	7 45	8 30	9 15
6	10 48	11 33	12 18	1 3	1 48	2 33	3 18	4 3	4 48	5 33	6 18	7 3	7 48	8 33	9 18	10 3
7	11 36	12 21	1 6	1 51	2 36	3 21	4 6	4 51	5 36	6 21	7 6	7 51	8 36	9 21	10 6	10 51
8	12 24	1 9	1 54	2 39	3 24	4 9	4 54	5 39	6 24	7 9	7 54	8 39	9 14	10 9	10 54	11 39
9	1 12	1 57	2 42	3 27	4 12	4 57	5 42	6 27	7 12	7 57	8 42	9 27	10 12	10 57	11 42	12 27
10	2 0	2 45	3 30	4 15	5 0	5 45	6 30	7 15	8 0	8 45	9 30	10 15	11 0	11 45	12 30	1 15
11	2 48	3 33	4 18	5 3	5 48	6 13	7 18	8 2	8 48	9 33	10 18	11 3	11 48	12 33	1 18	2 3
12	3 36	4 21	5 6	5 51	6 36	7 21	8 6	8 51	9 36	10 21	11 6	11 51	12 36	1 21	2 6	2 51
13	4 24	5 9	5 54	6 39	7 24	8 9	8 54	9 39	10 24	11 9	11 54	12 39	1 24	2 9	2 54	3 39
14	5 12	5 57	6 42	7 27	8 12	8 57	9 42	10 27	11 12	11 57	12 42	1 27	2 12	2 57	3 42	4 27
15	6 0	6 45	7 30	8 15	9 0	9 45	10 30	11 15	12 0	12 45	1 30	2 15	3 0	3 45	4 30	5 31
16	6 0	6 45	7 30	8 15	9 0	9 45	10 30	11 15	12 0	12 45	1 30	2 15	3 0	3 45	4 30	5 31
17	5 12	5 57	6 42	7 27	8 12	8 57	9 42	10 27	11 12	11 57	12 42	1 27	2 12	2 57	3 42	4 27
18	4 24	5 9	5 54	6 39	7 24	8 9	8 54	9 39	10 24	11 9	11 54	12 39	1 24	2 9	2 54	3 39
19	3 36	4 21	5 6	5 51	6 36	7 21	8 6	8 51	9 36	10 21	11 6	11 51	12 36	1 27	2 6	2 51
20	2 48	3 33	4 18	5 3	5 48	6 13	7 18	8 2	8 48	9 33	10 18	11 3	11 48	12 33	1 18	2 3
21	2 0	2 45	3 30	4 15	5 0	5 45	6 30	7 15	8 0	8 45	9 30	10 15	11 0	11 45	12 30	1 15
22	1 12	1 57	2 42	3 27	4 12	4 57	5 42	6 27	7 12	7 57	8 42	9 27	10 12	10 57	11 42	12 27
23	12 24	1 9	1 54	2 39	3 24	4 9	4 54	5 39	6 24	7 9	7 54	8 39	9 14	10 9	10 54	11 39
24	11 36	12 21	1 6	1 51	2 36	3 21	4 6	4 51	5 36	6 21	7 6	7 51	8 36	9 21	10 6	10 51
25	10 48	11 53	12 18	1 3	1 48	2 33	3 18	4 3	4 48	5 33	6 18	7 3	7 48	8 33	9 18	10 3
26	10 0	10 45	11 30	12 15	1 0	1 45	2 30	3 15	4 0	4 45	5 30	6 15	7 0	7 45	8 30	9 15
27	9 12	9 57	10 42	11 27	12 12	12 57	1 42	2 27	3 12	3 57	4 42	5 27	6 12	6 57	7 42	8 27
28	8 24	9 9	9 54	10 30	11 24	12 9	12 54	1 39	2 24	3 9	3 54	4 39	5 24	6 9	6 54	7 39
29	7 36	8 21	9 6	9 51	10 36	11 21	12 6	12 51	1 36	2 21	3 6	3 51	4 36	5 21	6 6	6 51
30	6 48	7 33	8 18	9 3	9 48	10 33	11 18	12 1	12 48	1 31	2 18	3 3	3 48	4 33	5 18	6 3
	vveft.	w. and by N.	w.N. weaft	N.we. by we	N.w.	N.w. by N.	N.N. weaft	N. & by w.	Nor.	N. & by Ea.	N.N. Eaft.	n.e. & by N.	N.E.	n.e. & by ea.	E.N. Eaft.	N. and by E.

THE COASTES OF THE MOONE
from the Full vnto the Chaunge.

Place this Table before the leafe. 153.

with your towne, and ouer againſte th'age of the Mone
you ſhall haue the daye, and houre, when as in that coſte
it is full ſea. As for example, I finde at Yermouthe.S.E. *An example.*
Wherby J ſaye that à Southeaſt Mone, make à full ſea
with them: thē J Imagine the Mone to be. xij.dais olde
therfore in the firſte rowe I ſeke th'age of the Mone, &
in the hier part of the Table, find S.E:then deſcending
yntill I be directly againſt th'age of the Mone, J find vi.
hours.xxxvi.minutes, which is the exact time, whan as
it is full ſea at Yermouthe. So in like manner you maye
worke with any place, about this our Ocean ſea, as in the
table goyng before it is euident.

Spoude. This J do right well perceiue.

Philon.   Now order inforſeth, that we conuert oure
talke ynto the windes, becauſe of the neceſſary yſe of thē
in Nauigation, & firſt you ſhall ynderſtande that the
winde is no other thing, then à hot & dry exhalatiō, in- *What the*
gendred in the bowels of th'Earth, which once breaking *winde is.*
forth, is driuen rounde aboute the face of the ſame.
This bothe Homer, and th'olde Græcians, deuided
only into.iiij.Eaſt, Weaſt, North & South. But thoſe *Foure Princi-*
that folowed them next, after à more exquiſite ſort, de- *pall windes.*
uided the Horizont into.viij.equall portions.

Spoud.   And what names did they deuiſe for them?

Philon.   I will ſhewe you, they called th'Eaſt:Subſola-
nus, for that the ſunne riſeth there being in th'equinoctiall poyntes. The Weaſt wind alſo they called Fauonius, of noriſhinge:the winde whiche commeth out of the
North, Septentrio:the South winde Auſter. Then the
winde

wind that bloweth betwixt th'eaſt, & the South, named South Eaſt. Alſo that which cōmeth out of that place betwixt th'eaſt & the north, they called it northeaſt. The ſpace directly betwixt the north, & the weſt, they named northweſt: as betwixt the ſouth, & the weſt ſouthweſt, as

in this, figure A. B. C. D. repreſent the Horizōt, A. th'eaſt, B. the north: C. the weaſt, D. the ſouth: E. the northeaſt: F. the nortweſt: G. the ſoutheaſt: & H. the Southeaſt. Spo. Yet ther is another kind of partinge the Horizōt, thē you haue declared: for I remember

that I red in Marcus Manilius, how the Horizōt was parted in 12. partes: but the reaſon of it I could neuer vnderſtande. His verſis as I remember, are theſe.

Aſper ab axe ruit Boreas: furit Eurus ab Ortu:
    Auſter amat medium Solem: Zephyruſq: profundum.
Hos inter binæ mediis è partibus auræ.
    Expirant ſimiles, mutato nomine, flatus.
From the North, rough Boreas come: & Eurus, from th'Eaſt:
    Auſter, from the South bloweth: & Zephyrus, from the VVeſt.
Betwixt either of theſe quartes, two other windes broſt out:
    In nature like: their names changed, whiſtling all th'earth about.
Phi.   Manilius doeth very aptly ſhew th'order of parting the Horizōt in to 12. partes. For (ſaith he) ther commeth two windes frō thoſe partes of the Horizont, where th'equinoctial croſſeth it equally, of which, th'Eaſt he calleth Eurus: And the Weaſt Zephyrus, or Fauonius. Thē the meridiā circle croſſeth alſo the Horizōt equally

in the middes. And so by these intersectiõs ther are *two*
other windes described: the North, he calleth Boreas,
The Southe Auster.

Spoud.. These. iiij. are the Principall windes, & a-
greeth with Homer & th'olde Gretians.

Philo. Yea, but in the rest it differeth bothe from thē.
& also the seconde sort. For these parted the Horizont
in. 8. equall portiõs: but Manilius into. 12. inequal parts
for he described. iiij. collaterall windes by the. ij. Tropick
Circles, which are the places where the Sonne riseth &
goeth downe in the middes of Somer, and Winter. And

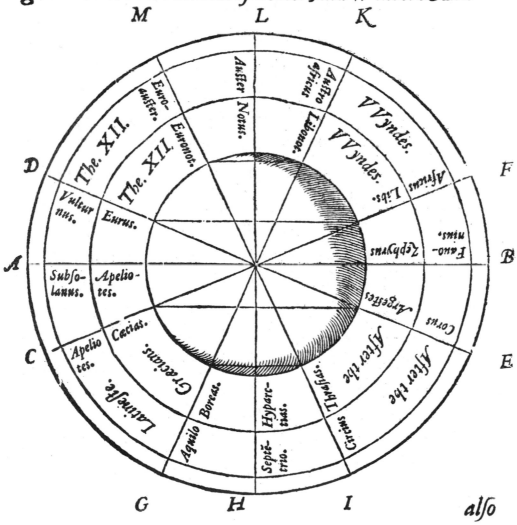

also

also other 4.winds at the Circles Arctick & Antarctick.
Spou. I remember that in our first daies talk, you shewed me what th'equinoctiall, the Tropickes, & the circles
Arctik & Antarticke were: notwithstanding I shall the
more spedely conceiue your meaning, if you vouchsafe (as
hetherto you haue vsed to geue me some example & picture hereof.

Phil. That I will not refuse to do, or any other thinge,
so that the more vtiliti hereof may vnto you insue. Wher
fore behold the tipe before placed in which. A.B.C.D.
E.F.G.H. Is the place of the Horizont. H. the Northe. A. th'East: L. the Southe: &.B. the Weast. From
which the Principall windes doth blowe. C. is the place
wher the Sonne riseth in the Sommer, & E. wher in the
same time of the yeare he setteth: Also. D. do represent
the place, where as the sonne riseth in the winter poynte,
and F. the coaste where he goeth downe. Also that
part of the Arctick circles, which is most easterly marked
with G, & th'other part furdest Weast, noted wyth I.

The Horizont
parted into 32
partes.
also the part of the Circle Antartike furdest East, is marked with M. And th'other portion furdest west with K.
But nowe in oure time, the learned Hydrographers, &
Trauelours on the Seas, haue yet gone beyonde them all,
partyng the Horizont in 32. equall portions, as sufficiet-
ly answering vnto euery viage throughe the hole Earth,
& they haue geuen them very apte names, as in this Instrument folowyng more largely appeareth.

Spou. Thus I see, that by diligence, & laboure,
small thinges haue great roote, & increasing. For firste
there

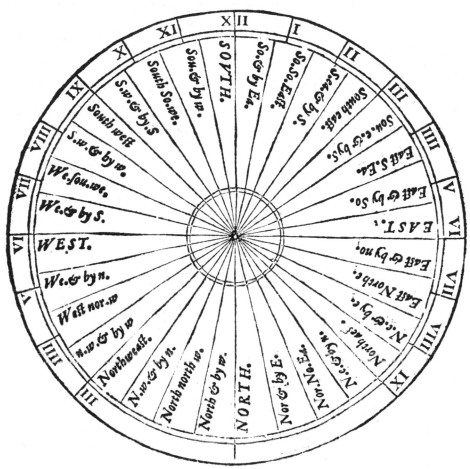

there were founde out but iiij. Cardinall, & cheif windes: after they wer made viij. in numbre, then xii. And
now in our dayes 32. so that I beleue we be at the furdest,
and that those whiche folow vs, shall not be able to adde
any thing to this pertition of windes. Phi. You are much
deceiued, if that you so do think, for the nūber of windes
be infinite, & breke out of euery part of the horizōt. But
like as 12. in nūber semed not sufficēt: so 32. ar thought to
answer in all parts, that is in Nauigatiō required, &
the deuisinge of à greater number, shall rather cause
confusion of memorie: then helpe in this behalfe.   Also
by this Compasse (the Sonne shynynge) you shall perfitly

The number
of windes in-
finite.

P.i.   know

know the houre of the day by the coaſt he is in. As when
he is right Eaſte, & Weſt, it is alwaye ſixe of the cloke:
alſo, à Southe Sonne maketh xij. of the clocke. So in
like maner, à ſoutheaſt ſonne, maketh ix. of the cloke, &
à ſouth weaſt ſonne, iij. of the cloke after noone. Th'other
houres are maniſeſt by the compaſſe.

Spou.   This is very neceſſary alſo in trauilinge. And
nowe retourne to that, from whence we did digreſſe.
Ther are certein qualities applied to the windes, wherof
doth that ſpringe?

Phi.   There are ſo, & that cometh of the tēperature
of th'Earth, ſo that the North windes be called coulde,
becauſe they procede frō the froſen Zone, & theſe ſouth
windes hote, becauſe that they come frō the burnt zone.
But this belōgeth more to Phyſick, thē Nauigatiō. For
we ſeke herin, to learne th'apt winde which ſhall cary vs,
vnto the deſired Porte, & not health, which is the Phy-
ſitions chiefe care.

Spou.   J cōfeſſe no leſſe, but yet ſence we haue entred in
to this matter, J wyll be ſo bold, as to trouble you herein
further. And where as you ſay, the qualities of the windes ſpring of the tēperature of th'earth, do you meane the
zones, & Climates?

Phil.   J do no leſſe: Spou.   Thē ſeyng the North
winde is called cold, becauſe it cometh frō the north froſen zone, why by the like reaſon ſhall not the South windes be of like qualitie, cōming frō the ſouth froſen zone?

Philoni.   J wyll aunſwer you in few wordes. The
North winde commeth from the North froſen zone,
and

North windes
colde.

South windes
hote.

An obiection

Th'Anſwere.

and is felt in our Climate, becaufe we are fituated, nerer that, then the South frofen Zone: whiche beinge vnder our fete (as you haue heard before declared) is kepte frō vs, & the couldnes of the winde, not only mitigated, but alfo greatlye altered, throughe the heate of the burninge Zone. And therfore the South windes are called hotte.

Spou. This doth very well agre both to reafon, & experience. So that in th'Equinoctial, wher both the north, and South windes meete, there the windes are called tē-perate, becaufe the couldnes of them is taken away by the heat of the burninge Zone. And by this alfo I gather, that fuche as dwell in the temperate Southe Zone, (Κ'υπιύχχατος Proclus call it) beyond th'Equinoctiall, they call the South wind cold, and the North wind hot.

Windes temperate vnder th'eqninoctiall

Phi. It muft neades fo be, for that the burninge Zone qualifieth the coldnes of the Northe windes, throughe his heat, as to vs, he doth the South.

Spou. There is now an other dout entred into my hed, of which to be deliuered I muft (or we furder proced) require your ientill aid. And that is, whether in defcribing the. iiij. Cardinall windes, you call the North Pole, the furdeft North poynt or not: and th'Antarctick Pole the South poynte.

A queftion.

Philon. No verely, refpecting our climate, but I call North, & South, the place of the Horizōt, which the meridiā circle rightly doth croffe, as alfo th'eaft, & weft, wher th'Equinoct. croffeth the horizōt. Spo. Thē vnder th'equinoctial, where the Poles are equall with th'earth

Th'Anfwere.

P.ij.　　the

the Poles them felues are the north & South poyntes.
Phil.   It mufte of force fo be. But now feinge
theis inftructions feme fufficient vnto you, touchinge the
order, number, diuifion, and names of the windes: I will
paffe from that, and conuerte my talke, vnto the defired
fcope, (that is) howe to directe anye fhippe, from place to
place, from Port to Port, exactly by Art:
Spou. And that is a thinge, whiche femeth merueilous.
For it is thought praife worthye to go by lande, directlye
without errour, from one place to an other, farre diftant
a fonder, hauing no path, or waye whereby to be guided.
But in the wide Ocean, to finde à direct way, & to con-
ducte his veffell vnto the port defired, is much more com-
mendable. If Vliffes had knowne this Art, he fhoulde not

Vliffes.

haue hene fo long toffed on the troublous feas. If Diome-

Diomedes.
Aneas.

des, or Æneas, had bene herein learned, they had not fo
manye yeares bene driuen from place to place: knowinge
not by what meanes, to attaine to their fo longe defired
Region. What thing more commodious for Princes, was
there euer inuented: more profitable for à comon weale:
and more neceffary for al men? And that confidering the
worthye Princes in time pafte, called Neptunus th'inuentor hereof, à God: as alfo Æolus, which found out the

Neptunus.
Æolus.

vfe of windes: For it is truely faid, honor norifheth artes.
Philon. I wold in thefe daies, they woulde reward the
learned, & painful (which ether inuent, or adde to that
which is inuented) with à neceffary liuing, & as for calling thē gods, let that paffe, it is to great a title for mor-
tall men. But omit we thefe thinges, as touchinge the
                                  direc-

directing of anye shippe, you maye do it two waies: th'one
by the compasse onely, whiche was to th'olde Hydrographers, vnknowne: th'other by longitudes, Latitudes, and
the compasse, of which herafter we will shew the maner.
As touchinge the firste waye, I will not laboure to write
much of, becaufe it is knowne well nie to euery Mariner.
But yet I will shewe them certain obseruations, by whiche there is found manye errors in the nedle: that done I
will also declare, how they shall correct the same, and fail
more exactly then the moft part are able?

Spou. Thys is à merueilous nedle, whiche beinge tou-
ched, (as I heare onlye with the Magnes) shoulde
knowe to turne alwaye to the North pole, and that only
by the same, the .iiij. Plages, and quarters of th'Earthe,
are presentlye founde oute. But what be th'obseruations
of this neadle, by whiche you affirme that it doth not exactlye poynte Northe, and Southe.

Phi. They are of Iofrancus sette forthe, in thys wise.
In the Ilande called Insula Corui, it declined Easterlye. xv. degrees. Also in the place which shipmen call (Le
Cap d'espoir en terre neuue) it declineth towarde the
Weaste. 33. degrees, and. 45. minutes. Againe at Deppe,
(faithe he) it poynteth Easterlye to much, by. 11. degrees
well nie.

Spo. If this be certain, then in dede th'error is not tol-
lerable, but admit it be not fo much, yet error in all thinges (as much as is possible) is to be eschewed, & veritie to
be folowed. Wherfore I pray you, shew me how to find out
à perfait nedle, & to correct it, if it be not perfect.

P. iij.   Phi.

The compasse
vnknowen to
th'olde Hydro
graphers.

The praise of
the neadle.

Obseruations
of the nedle
where it hath
erred.

Phi. Both the chosing of a nedle that is perfit, & also to correct the false, consisteth all in one precept. For if I can correct a false nedle, I can also chuse a true, & perfit: the way how you shall do that, is on this wise. whē you will verifie your nedle (if it be in the daye) you shall vse the healpe of the Sunne (and on the night) of some fixed sterre, marking diligently whā they are in the nonestead line: & then direct your nedle vnto the Sonne, or sterre, & if the flower of the nedle be righte Northe from it, your neadle is perfit: or if the flower be toward the sonne, & th'other part of it North, it is also true, & this your nedle corrected, you shall perfitly directe your ship, without errour. Spou. I can with my Astrolabe, or Quadrāt, obserue the height of the sōne, & sterre, vntill that he come to the meridiā, or nonestead line (as you taught me in the secōd dais talk) & at that instāt, place my nedle right towards him. Phi. And this wil serue as wel on the seas, as on the lād. But on the lād you may draw a meridiane line, as I taught you, & set your cōpasse on the meridian Line, which you haue drawen, in suche maner, as the line North & South in the compasse, stand right in thē same, & it is of all other th'exacte waye: & this hauinge youre line made, you maye at all times, verify any nedle, not tarying for the sonnes comming to the Meridian Circle.

Spou. But then my Meridian line whiche I haue drawē, must euer be fixed in some place without remouīg Philo. It must neades folow. Ther is also great error committed in describing the shipmans Cart, because thei

vse

vſe right lines in the place of Parallele circles, of which at this time I will no further intreate.

Spoud.   Then I praye you begin the waye how to ſaile by Longitudes, and Latitudes.

Philon.   Vnto this way are required the circles of the Spheare, the meridian altitude of the ſonne by daye, and ſterre by nighte, the heighte of the Pole, the longitude of Regions and Portes, and the vſe of the ſhipmans qua-drat, whoſe inuentor was worthy D. Gemma.

The greater Longitude.   The leſſer Longitude.

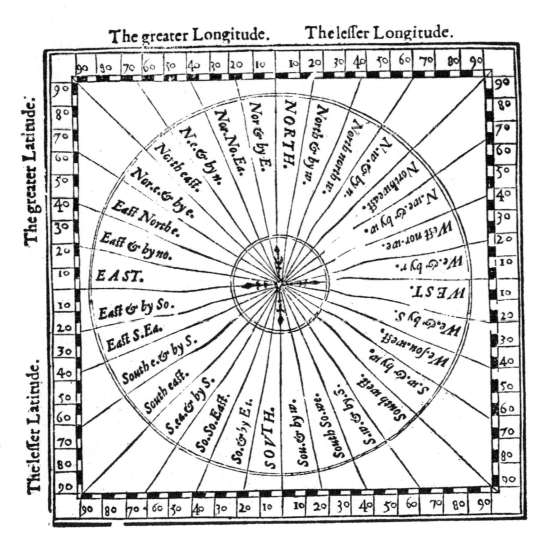

Spou.   As touching the Circles of the ſpheare, you gaue me inſtructiõs in our firſt daies talke: alſo to find th'altitude of the Pole, ſonne, & ſterre in the ſecond daies meting: the longitude of places you promiſed to ſet forth by them ſelues & geue me at my departure: therfore ther, only remain, to ſhew me th'uſe of the quadrat, in this art. Phi.   Thē I will herin ſatisfie your expectatiõ & finiſh our talke for this preſent. This Quadrat as you ſe conteineth.32. poyntes, with their names in them written. Spoud.   I perceiue it wel, but what is ment by thoſe degrees of Lõgitude, & Latitude, in that order placed? Philon.   I will ſhew you, opening the whole Art of directing your ſhippe. Firſt you muſt ſeke out the longitude

Howe to direct a ſhippe to any Porte.

& Latitude both of the place from whence you ſaile, & alſo of that vnto which you intend to trauaile. Thoſe you ſhall for the moſte parte finde in my boke (whiche I will deliuer you at our departing) then ſubtracte the ſmaller number of Longitude and Latitude oute of the greater, and with the differēce of Lõgitude and Latitude, do in this maner. Firſt if the Longitude of the place vnto whiche you trauell be greater then that from which you depart, entring into the hier part of the Quadrate (and towarde the left hande vnder thys title, the greater longitude) you ſhall ſeeke oute in degrees and minutes, thys difference. And do in like maner in the lower part of the table directly vnder it, & this difference ſo founde oute, apply à thride, or ruler, to the number founde in the hier part of the Quadrat, & alſo in the lower part.

Spou.

Spou.   But & if the Longitude of the place vnto whiche I trauell, be leſſe, thē that from whiche J departe ſhall J not then accompt the difference of Lōgitude from the middle Line, toward the right hand?

Ph. You muſt ſo do, but now as touching the difference in Latitude of the two places, if the pole of the place (vnto which you direct your ſhippe) be greater, then the Pole of the place, from which you loſen then accomptinge frō the midde line vpward, vnder this title, the greater Latitude, & in like caſe toward the right hād, then draw and extend a thrid, or apply à rulers, vnto this nūber of latitud, & wher the. ij. thrides or rulers croſſe one an other, ther make à marke for it is the place which you deſire.   Spou.   But where ſhall be placed the port from which J muſt depart?

Phil.   In the Center, or mids of the Quadrat. So that if you applie à ruler frō the Center of the Quadrate, vnto th'interſectiō of the two thrides or rulers, it ſhalbe manifeſt what point or winde, you muſt vſe, vntill you haue finiſhed your courſe.

Spoud.   But admit the lōgitudes be not trewly obſerued, & ſo I ſhalbe deceiued, how ſhall J know when we haue ſailed the differēces in lōgitude of theis ij. places?

Phil.   That you may at all times without difficultie bring to paſſe, by finding out the height of the pole: which you may do in the day, by the height of the ſonne, at midday, or on the nyght, by ſome fixid Sterre: or (that Sterre which Shipmen call) the Lode Sterre.

Spoud.

Spou.   *How may I knowe the forme of this lode starre?*
Phil.   *Becauſe the forme of it ſhall much better make
you know it, then th'vſe of many wordes, behold here the
Figure folowing, in which you ſhall ſee the configuration
both of the Pole Arctick,
and alſo Antarctick. And
now againe to oure former
talke: hauing the height of
the Pole found oute by inſtrumẽt, you ſhall enter into the Quadrat with thys
number, findinge oute the
Latitude, frõ the midline,
vpward or downward, as before it was declared: & apply à ruler vnto the ſame place, noting diligentlye where
this ruler, toucheth the line whiche was drawne frõ the
center, vnto the interſectiõ of the difference of Lõgitude
and Latitude firſt taken. Thẽ accõpt the like number in
the differẽce of Lõgitude, that you did of Latitude, and
applying the ruler ther vnto, it ſhall ſhew plainly the lõgitude of that preſẽt place, like as the line from the center, do certainly declare the coſte of the worlde.*

A. Is the Sou-
the Pole,
D.C. th'Equi
noctiall.
B. the Northe.

Spou.   *This ſemeth to haue à ſinguler vſe in rectifyıng
the longitudes of places.   Nowe that, whiche here is
ſpoken, toucheth onlye th'exacte courſe (and as it were)
the pathe, in which we muſte ſaile. But if greate windes,
tempeſtes, and ſtormes ariſe, ſo that we are vtterly driuẽ
from oure courſe, toſſinge vp and downe, the Seas, howe
maye I knowe, in what Parallele, and Climate, we are,
that*

How to know
in what place
they are, beyng
driuen from
theyr courſe.

that therby we may come againe to our right courſe.

Phil.   That ſhall you do by the helpe of the Table of Fol.77.78.
Clymates, & Paralleles, in the ſeconde boke, & by the
Eleuatiõ of the Pole, the findyng of whiche I haue ſo of-
tẽ ſet forth, that I am aſhamed to make therof any more
mention.

Spou.   Then you will that hauinge the height thereof,
I ſhall enter into that table of Climates, & ſeke ther the
eleuatiõ, & directly againſt it, I ſhall finde the name of
the Paralleles, & Clymates.

Phil.   You do rightly vnderſtande my meanyng. And
theſe thinges parfaitly kept in memorie, & put in prac-
tiſe, when as occation ſhall be miniſtred: ther ar not many other thïges in this buſines requiſite. Wherfore, ſeyng
that ʃ haue ſatisfied your requeſt, in all ſuch thinges as
you at our firſt daies meting deſired, I thinke it à conuenient place, at this time to make an ende touchinge this
Argument of Coſmographie, Geographie, & Nauigation. And therfore depart with me, & you ſhall receiue
the Boke, which ʃ promiſed, conteinynge in it the Longitudes, & Latitudes of the famous Regiõs, Countreis,
Cities, Townes, Uillagies, & ſuche like, as ar placed on
the face oʃ th'Earth. And when you find any other doubtes, either in this Arte, or any other belonging to my pro-
feßion, if you do to me reſort, I will therin willingly helpe
you to my power.

Spoud.   ʃ thanke you moſt hartely, & thus haue
ʃ kept you (for my vtilities ſake) from your vrgent, and
ne-

necessary busines, this long season, & that without recei-
uing at my hand againe any recompēce. But sence I can
not do herein what my good will is, I shall referre the whole vnto God, who plētiously
rewardeth the good trauelles of
euery man.

THE FIFTHE BOOKE OF THE

COSMOGRAPHICAL GLAS, IN VVHICHE

the partes of th'Earthe, perticulerlye (accordinge to the late obseruations of Cosmographers in oure age) are exactlye described.
VVith the Longitudes and Latitudes of Regions, Prouinces, Ilandes, Cities, Townes, Villages, Hilles : also
the commodities of euerye Countrye, the natures of
th'Inhabitauntes, Lawes, Rightes, and Cu-
stomes, with diuers other thinges coinci-
dent to the same.

PERCHAVNCE, ther mai arise sundry sico-
phāts (reading this my la-
bour folowing) which will
not let to accuse me of arro
gancie, in that J take this
part in hand, sence Ptolomæus that famous Kinge
hath of that argument left
to vs his Geographie. Unto whome J answer, confessing
me not worthy to kisse his fotesteppes, aswell for the ma-
iestie of his person, whan he liued, as also for his excellent
Learning, Science, & diligence. But seinge the hougie-
nesse of the labor, did farre transcend not only his, but al
so the diligence of anye one man (hauing none other beginning then he had) he is to be excused, though he haue
not expressed throughoute his hole worke the true situation of places. For as touchinge this parte it is requisite,
ether to trauell muche him selfe, or els to take obseruations of the mooste learned, whiche dwell in the Regions,
for whiche he will wrighte.

Q.i.   But

But th'other part of his laboures touching the heauenlye motions (becauſe remaininge in one place) he might
beholde the Heauens, tourninge and ſhowinge them
ſelues, he hathe moſte exactlye not only laid the foundation, but alſo broughte it to perfecte ende, as the noble
Almegiſt dothe teſtiſie. But as touchinge this my booke
of Longitudes and Latitudes, I haue for the chief places of Englande vſed bothe my frendes trauailes, and
alſo mine owne obſeruations. And where as any place is
taken oute of Ptolomæus, that ſhall you find noted with
à ſtarre *. In whiche alſo thys I haue diligently obſerued
(hauinge. vi. ſondrye examples and Copies) that where
the mooſte parte of them agree, that I haue onlye vſed.
Alſo in deſcribinge other Regions, I haue folowed th'obſeruations of th'inhabitantes. As in Frauce, I haue vſed
authours, which are French men: For Spaine, Spaniardes: in Germany in like caſe Germaines: And in the late
founde Ilandes, ſuche as do of them moſt probably treat.
Moreouer, I haue for the moſte parte, placed to euery
Citie, Towne, & Porte, two names, th'one Latin for the
cõmunitie of the tõgue, th'other as it is properly of th'inhabitauntes named. And if I ſhal not exactly for the difficultie of the worke in all places expreſſe the perſite Lõ-
gitudes & Latitudes: Thou muſte herein pardon me
(frendly Reader) for the cauſe aledged, & alſo take
this in good parte, ſeynge no man (Ptolomæus excepte)
hetherto haue in all partes ſet oute ſo large, & ample à
worke. But now I will cõmit it to thy deſcretion & iudgement.

A per-

A PERTICVLER DESCRIPTION OF
Europe: VVhich in our daies conteineth Chriſtendome and part of Turkie.

Eing that th'Earthe inuironed, and compaſſed with the mightye Ocean ſeas, ſemeth as it were an Iland: th'ancient Geographers (for the better auoyding confuſió in the deſcribing of the face of the earth) deuided it into .iij. partes, Europe, Africke and Aſia. As for the fourthe parte, whiche is called America or the newe worlde, was vnto them vnknowne. Therfore at this preſente, mindinge to folowe the ſame order, I will firſt begin with Europe. This parte was ſo called as hiſtories do witneſſe, of an amiable Ladye called Europa being daughter to King Aginor, whoe Iupiter (being rauiſhed with her beuty) eſpying among à companye of other virgins, playinge by the ſea ſide caried away out of Africke, ſaylinge throughe the Ponticke Seas vntyll he came into Crete. This ſtorie the Poëtes in this wiſe do reſite, how that Iupiter turned into à white Bul, did cari hir on his back thorow the ſeas into Crete, which bul was no other thing thē that in their Enſigns, & Flagges, the Cretētiãs nauie bare the white Bul. This part of th'erth is pleaſantly ſeparated from Africk, by the middle earth Seas, which is ſo named of ſundry Nations, that it noriſheth. It is alſo parted from Aſia, by the notable Riuer Tanais, whiche from the North partes with great violence runneth into Ponte Euxine.

Q ij.   The

The Heauens in this part giueth temperatnes of Aëre: th'Earth flowing with aboundance of all thinges necessary for mans vse. As Graines, Fruites, Fiſhe, Foule, Oyles, Wines, Catell, Metalles, & ſuche like. The nature of the people more ciuill, frindlyke, wiſe, learned, & apter vnto warres then they of Afrike, & Aſia. And although it may ſeme much inferior to them, if you do conſider the bignes, & quantitie: yet in the commodities to it belonging, it ſhalbe to either of them equiualẽt. Morouer it is beautified with pleaſaũt Ilandes, adorned with notable Riuers, & finally garniſhed with innumerable Cities, Townes, Fortreſſes, & Villages. The length (by directe diſtaunce from the vttermoſte confines, & borders of Spaine, vnto Conſtantinople in Græce the furdeſt place Eaſt of all Europe) conteineth after Ptolomæus minde 2200. Engliſhe miles: the breadth of it to be ſomwhat leſſer Ptolomæus affirmeth. Notwithſtanding, if you rekẽ the Septentrionall Regiõs, which ware to Ptolomæus vnknowen, as Sueulande, Gothlande, Norway, & other ſuch, you ſhal well perceiue the Latitude to excede the length of the ſame. Ther are alſo in Europe many perticuler Regions, as Englande, Irlande, Scotlande, Spayne, Fraunce, Germany, Italy, Polande, Vnlgarie, Denmarke, Græce, & diuerſe, vnto the nũber (as Ptolomæus affirmith) of 34. Of whiche ſeuerallye I will ſet out the notable Cities & townes, mountaynes, & riuers, beginning with Irland firſt, as Ptolomæus doeth in his Geographie.

OF

OF IRLANDE.

Irland is an Iland very fertile, subiect to the Crowne of Englad: In it ther ar great plētie of wolues, red Alume, sea Cole, also mines of gold, & siluer, & in sūdry places Pearles are foūd. It bringeth forth very many herbes necessarye for the healthe of man. It is free from Venomous beastes, & Wormes, as Ranny, Tode, Edder, Snack, swift, or such like. The people are sauage, wilde, & beastly, they are giuen to sorcerie, superstitiō, & witchcraft: their shirtes, & smokes are saffroned, they go with long Mantils, Their weapons in battel are Darts, & swords, which are brodest at the point: theyr musicall Instrumētes in battell, are Bagpipes. They delight in many coloured fring. They are great drinkers of Aqua vitæ (which is ther only medicine.) They liue vnto 60.70. And (as I here) vn-

to 90. yeares. The longitude of it, is supposed to be 280. Englishe miles, & the breadth, 92. miles. The middes of this Ilande hath in longitude, & latitude. 7.0.57.0.   The chiefe places are

*The north pmontorie. 13.0.61.0
*Venicnium promontorie. 12.50. 61.20.
Reba.   6.40.57.20.
Lamon.   7.5.56.30
S. Patrickes Purgatory 6.42.58.50
*Diuiline, Eblana.   14.0.59.0

There are ioyninge vnto Irlande, fiue Ilandes called Ebudæ, but of Plinie, Hæbudes. Of which that whiche is most west, is called properlye
*Ebuda.   15.10.62.0

That which is moste East.
*Ebuda·   15.20.62.0
Ricnea.   17.0.62.0
Maleos.   17.30.65.10
Epidium   18.30.62.0

Also on th'east part of Irlande, are these Ilandes
*Monarina   17.40.61.30
*Th'Ile of Man   15.0.57.20
*Adros, a desert.   15.0.59.20
Limnus, a desert.   15.0.59.0

OF ENGLANDE.

Englande the most famous and plentifull Iland in all the

Earth of *Ptolomæus* called *Albion*, afterward *Britãnia secunda:* Bicauſe that in the daies of *Ptolomæus*, *Scotlãd* & it were accompted for one *Flande*, It is inuironed about with th'Oceã Seas, not much vnlike to à *Triãgle* in ſhape: it hath on th'*Eaſt* parte of it, *Germany*, on the *South Eaſt*, *Fraunce*, on the *Weaſt*, *Frelande*, & on the *North*, the 30. *Flandes*, called *Orchney*. Of *Englande*, both of the finding of it firſte, & alſo of the perticuler deſcription, herafter, I ſhall more largly ſpeak (if God graunt life.) At this time, I intend but onely to ſet out the *Longitude*, & *Latitude* of the chiefe *Cities*, & *Townes*, as here foloweth.

*Bathe, Aquæ calidæ. 17.30.53.40
*Bangor, Ganganotum. 15.30.57. 30.
Berwicke.Tueſis.   17.0.56.50
*Bodnam.Voliba.   14.50.52.20
Bedforde.   21.0.52.0.
Bukhingham.   21.0.52.50
Bury.   22.20.52.0
Callis.Caletum.   25.10.51.40.
Caërleil.Caturaƈonium   19. 30.58.0

Caëmarden.Maridunum   15. 30.54.40

🐦 *Cambridge*, à *Vniuerſitie* floriſhing with al kind of good letters.   21.30.52.0
Canterbury.   22.10.51.10
Cheſter. Vſellum.   18.30.52.10
*Chicheſtre. Næomagus.   19. 43 53.35.
Colcheſtre.Camulodanum.   21.0. 51.40
Couentrie.   20.0.52.0
Darbie.   20.0.54.10
*Dee.Deua,a riuer.   17.0.60.0
Doncaſter.Deuana.   18.30.55.0
*Doram.Dunum Sinus.   20.45. 57.30.
Elye,an Ile.   21.36.52.15
Exceſtre.Iſca.   17.30 52.15
Glouceſtre.   18.0.54.30
Harforde   20.0.52.50
Humber.Abus,a riuer.   21.0.56 30.
Huntington.   21.0.53.20
Hulle.   21 10.54.34
Kirkby.Olicana.   19.0. 57.30
Lancaſtre   19.0.55.0
Leiceſtre.   19.40.52.50
Lincclne.Lindum.   18.20.55 10.

🐦 *Londõ* of *Ptolomæus* called *Lõdinium*, is the chief & principall citie of all th'Iland, it is exceding populous, it is inhabited with men of euerye facultie, it was builded before *Rome*.420.yeare, before

fore the reign of *Alexander the great.*811.*yeres,& befor Christ our sauiors incarnatiõ* 1136. *so that from the firste buildinge of it, the yeares are* 2735 . *And whereas Cities throughe processe of time do come to ruine & decay:this Citye contrariwise do more and more beautifye and increase. the Longitude & Latitude.*

19.52.51.30.

Manchester.Mediolanium.	16.45 .56.40.
S.Michaels mounr.	12.0.51.30
New Castell.Orrea.	19.20 58.55
North Hampton.	21.0.52 15

Norwiche an healthfull & pleasant Citye , hauinge à faire Riuer called Yerus, ronning thorow it , which cometh out of the seas, frõ Yermouthe coste. It is much subiect to fiers , which haue not à little hindred the beuty therof.The picture of it you shall find liuely set out in the firste boke:the longitude & Latitude.22.30.52.10..

Notyngham.Hrate.	18.0. 55.30.

Oxenford called (of Ptolomæus) Caleua à norishe of learning, and à famous vniuersitie it is in Longitude & Latitude. 19.0.51.50.

Penbrouch.	16.0.53.40
Peterborough.	21.0.53.20
Portsmouth,	19.0.51.20
Richmunde	19.0.55.20
Sandwich.	21.45.5.6
Salisbury.	19.0.51.50
Seuerne,a riuer.	17.20.54.30
Sudburie.	21.20.51.55
VVinchester.	21.30.50.15
VVight,an Ilande.	19.20 5.20
Yermouth.	22.20.52.20.
Yorke.	19.0.54.20
Ypswich.	22.0.52.40
Tynemouth.	24.0.58.30
Tenet,an Iland.	23.0.54 20.

OF SCOTLANDE.

*S*cotland being reconed of *Ptolomæus,* but for part of Albion is parted by two armes of the seas,which mete not from England.Th'east arme begin about.ij.miles from the minster of Eburcuring: the weast arme on the right side,à strõg Citie Aclynd(whiche in the Britishe tongue ,was called the Riuer Clynt.

Q iiij. The

The chiefe cities, & townes, are these folowyng.

S.Andrewes.	16.40.57 55.
Dunber. Varer	17.0.59.30.
Dundie.	19.20.59.30
Dunkel.	19.20.58.0

Edenbrugh called Alata castra is the chief Citie in all Scotlande. 17.15.59.20

Saint Iohns 15.40.59.15

Also the middes of the 30. Flandes adiacent to Scotlãd, called Orchney. 30.0.61.40

OF ISLANDE.

Island called of Ptolo. Thyle, is an Ilãde subiecte to the king of Denmarke: it is full of maruailous thinges to beholde. Amonge whiche ther are iij. mountaines of an incredible height: the toppes of which ar cõtinually couered with snow. The first mountaine is called Helga: the seconde, the moũt of the Crosse: the thirde, Hecla, which cõtinually (like to the mountaine Ætna) doeth burne, castig with violẽce (as it were out of à Gũne) greate stones frõ it. And this fire can not by water be quẽched, & that which is to be wondred, although the fire be marueylus great, & of force, by reason of the Sulphure, yet haye straw, or rede, is not of it cõsumed. Sulphure is there so plẽtifull that you may for the 4. part of à ducate, haue a thousande weight. There are also 4. Foũtaines of à diuerse nature, & qualitie. The first, if you cast in à sticke, mã, beast, or what soeuer it be, it torneth it presently into à stone, yet it reteineth the naturall forme still. The seconde is of an intollerable could. The third is much sweter then Hony, & most pleasãtly aswageth drines. The fourth is Pestilent, Poisonable, & deadly. Whã as the Sonne is in the beginning of Cancer, it is continual day with them, & whan he is in Capricorne, also continuall night

night, & darknes. They are à simple people, & hould the the faith of Chriſt. Thei haue no king, but all obey the Biſhoppe as theyr kinge. Their marchandiſe are Fiſhe, wad-moll, & ſulphur. There are found Falcons, Sperhaulkes, Crowes, Beares, & Wolues, both white & blacke. Roũde about this Flãd, for the ſpace of 6.or 7.mõthes, th'Iſe ſwim meth, makinge à miſerable ſound, & noiſe, ſo that th'inhabitauntes ſuppoſe that in the mount Hecla, & in this Iſe, the ſoules of men & women, are tormented. The fro ſen, & congelid Seas beginne at this Iland. It is now much trauailed to of engliſh mẽ, & Danes, & that in the Sõmer onely, becauſe of the horrible colde, & aboundance of Iſe. The middes of this Ilande

	7. 0.65.30.
Harſol, a Citie	7.40.60.42
Thirtes, a Citie.	5.50.64.44
Nadir, a Citie.	6.40.57.20

OF CORSICA.

Corſica, an Iland whoſe chiefe places are

Iſtria.	30.30.40.15
Mariana.	30.10.40.20
Nebia.	31.0 40.40
Aleria.	31 35.40.20

SICILIA.

Sicilia, an Ilande.

Palerna.	35.30.36.10
Marſara.	35.20.35.30
Gergentum.	36.20.35.10
Terminæ.	35.55.36.5
Pula.	36.0.36.0
Siracuſæ,	37.20.35.30
Cataua.	37.40.36.0
Meſsina.	38.0.36.40
Aetna, the burning hil.	37.10.35.20
20.	

OF THE CHIEF
Cities, & townes, in th'Ilande of Sardinia.

Ardos.	30.20.38.58
Galea.	29.40.37.50
Argetara.	29.30.36 30
Areſtana.	29 45.36.50
Aquilaſtrum.	31.20.37.30
Cambonara.	31.30 36.30
Stira.	30.30.36.40

OF TH'ILANDES
called Maiorica, & Minoria.

Maiorica, & Minorica, be Ilãdes adiacent to Spaine, & Maiorica conteineth in Lõgitude, & Lat. 17.40.38.30

Minorica.	20.0.39.0

GADRIA

GADIRA AN Ilande.

Adira, whiche is also called the Gades, in the weſt Oceã vnder 5.digr.30.34.0.

EVBOEA, AN Ilande.

EVbœa, nowe called Ni-gropont: Is an Ilande to Achaia ioyning.54.0.38.0.

CRETA, AN Ilande.

CReta, nowe called Can-die, an Ilande famous. 55.0.35.20.

CYCLADES.

CYclades, are Ilandes a-bout Delus.56.10.37.20

SPORADES Ilandes.

THeſe Ilandes are also ioynynge to Delus, they ly ſcatered about in the ſeas, of the read Plinius lib.4.ca-pite.xij.theyr Longitude, & Latitude.56.10.37.20

Thus endeth the perti-culer deſcription of the chief Ilands in Europe.

SPain as it appereth in the Table thereof in Ptolomæus Geo-graphie, it compaſſed aboute with the ſeas, excepte it be in that parte whyche toucheth Fraunce, and is parted from Fraunce by the Pyrenean mountains. And it is the firſt Region, Weaſt betwixte A-fricke & Fraunce. It brin-geth fourth ſuch aboundance of pleaſaunte fruictes, that it ſerueth not onlye the neceſſi-tye of it ſelfe, but alſo of Ita-lie and diuers other partes. They do not boyle their ſalt, as they do in Selande, but dig it oute of th'Earth. The men go all for the moſte parte in ſhorte clokes, and commenlye blacke. This Region in tyme paſte, was deuided into fiue Kingdomes, that is to ſaye, Gallicia, Nauarra, Caſtille, Catalonia, vnto which is ioy-ned Aragonie, Portugale & Granate. Of whiche we will

will perticulerlye touche the chiefe Cities, & townes, begynning with Castilla, whose principall Cities, & Townes are.

Tolet, where the famous king Alfonsus made his astronomicall Tables, conteining the mouinge of the heauenly Bodies.   10.49.37.0

Salamanca	7.20.38.20
Valeria now called Concha.	11.34.43.5.
Alcala de Enares.	10.20.41.40
Logronyo.	12.10.44.0
Valladolit.	10.10.42.0

GALLITIA.

Compostella, wher S. Iames is 7.0.42.15.

Landes end.	4.23.44.2
Almoisa.	4.40.44.45
Bilbao	11.45.45.25
Fontarrabie	13.13.44.15
S. Sebastianus	15.30.45.5

NAVARRE.

Pompelon	13.15.42.0
Vaganna	12.15.43.0

CATHALONIA.

New Carthage	15.57.38.0
Tarragone	16.12.41.0
Gerona	17.42.42.12
Barsalona	17.0.41.35
Valentia	14.38.36.10

ARRAGONIE.

Sarragossa	13.45.41.45
Burges.	10.33.42 48

PORTVGALE.

Lysbona	5.0.36.40
Portugallo	4.56.41.35

Arcobriga	5.40.36.35
Badaioz	5.20.39.0
Cabo de. S. Vincentio.	2.32.38.15
Braga	6.0.43.40
S. Maria de Guadalupe.	8.30.39.30

GRANATE.

Granate	8.34.34.20
Hispalis.	5.42.37.0
Corduba	7.4.37.50

Calpe, both one of the Pillors of Hercules, & also à moūtaine called at this daye Gilbalter where the streit is named Zibalter.   7.30.36.15

Vama	6.15.38.25
Malaga	8.50.37.30

OF FRAVNCE.

Fraunce beyng seperated from Spaine, by the Pyrenean Mountaines foloweth nexte. Jt is parted from England, by the Englishe Seas. Jt conteineth many dukedomes. It is garnished with pleasant Cities, & townes, of which I wil set out the principall: begining with the weast part first.

NARBONA HATH

Vienna.	26.0.45.0
Ebredunum.	28.8.43.30
Briansonum.	28 30.45.0
Gratianopolis. Granoble.	27.0.45 30.
Tarantasia.	29.0.45.0
Gebenæ.	28.0.45.45
Mauriana.	28.30.44.30

Va-

Vapincum.	27.15.43.30
Dinia.	27.35.43.5.
Valentia.	26.0.44.10
Romonum.	26.0.44.30
Siſtarica.	26.45.43.20
Viuarium	25.45.43.45.
Auraſicum	26.30.43.30
Auinio.	25.45.43.15
Carpentorate	26.5.43.15
Tritaſtra	25.45.43.0
Arelatum.Arles.	25.50.42.45
Maſsillia.	26.30.42.5
Tollona.	27.30.42.0
Barcellonna.	28.30.43.15

AQVITANIA.

Burdigala.	18.0.44.30
Baiona.	17.30.44.30
Vaſaticum.	18.15.44.0
Tarba.	19.15.42.15
Lorona.	18.10.42.0
Lebretum.	18.30.43.10
Auſcus.	20.15.43.0
Lombarium	21.20.42.40
Tholoſſa.	22.10.42.50
Rinum.	21.45.42.15
Conſerana.	22.15.41.50
S.Pontius.	23.0.42.15
Narbona.	23.30.42.0
Agata.	24.0.42.10
Mirapiſcæ	22.45.42.15
Lodeua.	23.45.42.50
Beſerium.	23.30.42.20
Mons peſſulanus,Monpeleier.	24.30.42.50.
Aſtrericum.	23.0.43.0
Vabra.	23.15.42.45
Varinum.	22.15.43.15
Albia.	22.30.43.40
Montalbanum.	21.30.43.30
Cadurcum.	22.0.44.0
Rhodium.	23.15.43.30
S.Florus.	23.30.44.0
Anicium.Lepny.	24.30.44.15

CELTICA GALLIA.

Lugdunum,Lyons.	26.0.45.15
Niuernium.	24.0.46.40.
Lamouica.	21.30.45.45
Petragoricum	21.15.44.40
Engoliſma	20.30.44.50
Xantona	19.0.45.0
Luxiona	18.30.46.30
Nanetum	18.15.47.15
Rhedona	17.30.48.10
Turonia Tours.	20.15.47.30
Aurelia orleans	22.0.47.30
Conſtantiæ	18.40.49.35

Lutetia Pariſiorum . Paris the head Citie of all Fraunce in which is à floriſhinge vniuerſitie,the fame where of is ſpreade throughe all Europe.

23.30.48.40.

Seno.	24.0.47.45
Cathalanum	25.30.48.30
Lingo	26.30.47.30

GALLIA BELGICA.

Rothomagus,Roan.	21.30.49.30
Catalaunum,Chaalō.	21.30.48.30
Rettena.Rethe.	22.26.49.0

GERMANYE.

Germany,the moſt ample,& large Regiō in in all Europe,ſomtime diuided frō fraūce,by the Rhine: from the Pannonians by the riuer Danubye,& from Sarmatia & Dēmarke, by moū taines,& Hilles,& in al other partes hauing th'Ocean Seas.But in our daies, it ex-

ten-it ſelfe more largely. It maye compare at this tyme wyth Spaine, Fraunce, or Italy, in cōmodities to it belōging. For it is beautified with moſt plea ſaunt Cities, Townes, & Ca- ſtels, it hath great woddes, a- boundance of fruites, & hils repleniſhed with plētiful Vi- nes. There are alſo theſe fa- mous, & helthfull riuers, the Rhine, Danuby, Moganus, Albis, Neccarus, Sala, O- dera, with diuers other. It is parted into the hier Germa- ny & into the lower, of which we will firſt ſet out the princi pall cities and Townes.

❧ Seelāde, an Ilād the fur- deſt cōſines of Germany the middes of it, in Longitud, & Latitude. 25.0.52.0.

Middlebourgh.   25.26.51.48

HOLLANDE.

Traieſtum, Vtrick.   27.15.52.20.

BRABANT.

A Ntuerpia, Antwerpen, the nobleſt Towne in all Europe.   26.36.51.28

Louaine, a vniuerſitie.   20.36 50.59.

Bruxella. Bruſſell	20.16.51.28
Mechlinia Machelen	20.20.51.15
Lira. Liere	20.24.51.21

FLAVNDERS.

Gandauum Ghent	23.30.51.15
Bruge brugge	24.30.51.20
Tornacum. Tornay	25.15.50.10

PICARDIE.

Ambianum Amiens	16.40.49.49
S. Iodocus	16.52.52.0
Samarobriga	22.20.52.10

LVCENBVRGE.

Lucenburgum	25.30.50.0
Creutznacum Creutz	24.34.50.2
Sarbruccū. Sarbruck	23.47.49.16
Keyſerluterna	24.44.49.22

GVLICH.

Bonna bonne	23.23.50.47
Iuliacūm Gulich	22.44.51.8
Leodium Ludich	21.48.50.51
Aquiſgranum Achen	28.45.50.55

GELDRIA.

| Geldria Gheldere | 23.48.51.42 |

CLEVIA.

| Cleuis. Cleff. | 22.6.52.0 |

HELVETIA.

s. Gallus	27.6.47.8.
Conſtantia	26.43.47.30
Tigurum Zurch	26.36.46.48
Badena Baden	25.16.48.44
Lucerna	26.0.46.34
Friburgum	37.30.51.50
Berna	24.18.46.25

ALSATIA.

Colmaria	24.3.48.12
seleſtadium schletſtad.	24.6. 48.22
Cæſarmontanum Keyſerſperg.	23 48.48.14
Hagenoia Hagenau	24.36.49.7

CITIES OF BASSE
Germanye.

R j.   Colo-

Colonia Agrip 29.45.51.0
Campena Kampen 28.30.52.50

Confluence, cõmonly called Coblentz, wher two faire riuers the Rhine, & Mosell mete. 30.15.50.20

Andernachum Andernacke. 30.0.50.25.

CITIES, AND TOVV-
nes of hie Germanie.

Maguntia, Mentz, the Bishoppes seat. At this Citie was th' Art of Printing first foũd (by Iohn Faustus) in the yere of Christ our sauiour. 1453. The Lon. & lati. 31.15.50.0

VVormatia, wormes.31.30.49.40
Spira Spier 31.30.49.15

Argẽtina, Strausborough à notable citie, in which Iohn Sturmius, & D. Seuenus excellẽt Orators florished 1559 30.15.48.45.

Basilia. Basile 29.45.47.45
Schathusa 28.0.47.28
Curia chur. 32.0.47.30
Vesalia 26.20.51.30
Francofordia 31.40.50.10
Curia 32.0.47.30
Marburgum 32.10.51.0
Bremen 32.10.53.40

Heydelbergũ, called Heydelberge, is à florishing Uniuersitie, mainteined by the

Palsgraue, by it ther rũneth the riuer Neccarus: ther florished 1559 in Phisicke, D. Iohn Langius, the Princes Phisician, Iacob Curio, Thomas Erastus, Petrus Lotichius Secundus, all Doctors in Phisick: And D. Balduinus the Reader of the Ciuill Lector, with diuers others, of whom I was very gentely interteined at the time of my Commensment.32. 0.49.30.

Vlmes 33.0.48.30
Herbipolis wirtzpurgk 33.30.50.0
Amberga 34.0.47.15
Augusta 34.0.48.15
Brunsuiga 34.40.52.40
Ingolstadium 34.45.48.30
Hamburgum 34.0.54.30
Limeburgum 34.45.5.45
Ratisbona 35.40.49.0
Erdfordia 35.0.51.10
Lubecum 35.20.54.50
Liptzigum 36.30.51.30
Magdaburge 36.10.54.50
Salisburgum 36.30.47.30
Brandenburgum 37.20.52.40
Rostochium 37.10.54.36
Misna 37.20.51.50
Peurbachium 37.35.48.15
Berlinum 38.30.52.50
Praga 38.20.50.6
Gripsualdia. 38.55.54.10
Vratislauia 41.20.51.5
Gran 42.50.47.15
Posna 42.0.52.45
Buda 43.0.46.50
Lonreth 43.20.52.30
Thorn

Thorn	43.30.53.30
Cracouia	44.30.50.15
Mons Regius	49 0.45.0
Dantiſcum	46.0.54.55
Caraloſtadium	33.25.50.0
Noribergum	34.40.49.30
Munſter	32.0.52.5
VVitenberga	32.10.53.40

MOSCOVIA.

MOſcouia is à longe & ample Regiŏ, the people miſerable, ſuſpicious, & craftie, the chief citie of ther Empirour is alſo called Moſkaua. 69.0.57.0. Thither ſailed out of England. 1553 Chancelour, & diuers other. The nature of th'inhabitantes, cŏmodities of the coŭtry, & à perſite deſcription of all the parts of the ſame you ſhal ſe at large ſet oute by Sigiſmunde Liber baron &c.

ILLIRIA, AND Dalmatia.

ILliria, which is called Lyburnia, hath on the North parts Pannonia, on the weſt Iſtria, on the South the Uenice ſeas, & on th'Eaſt Dalmatia the chiefe Cities, & townes are

Sara	40.5.44.9

Stridona the countrye of Saynt Ierome	42.20.43.20
Flauona	37.0.44.45

DALMATIA.

Raguſia	45.0.42.20
ſibinicum	43.0.43.20
ſcutara	45.30.41.30
ſaloniana	45.0.43.20
Durazo	45.55.40.55

ITALIE, AND LOMbardie.

Brunduſium	41.0.39.30
Tarentum	40.30.39.15
ſalernum	37.20.39.30
Naplis	38.50.39.55
Capua	36.40.40.5
Aquilea	36.40.41.10

Roma , à Citie famous through all th'Earth. 36.40.42.0

Sena	34.10.42.0
Florence	34.15 42.45
Viterbia	35.0.41.15
Piſa	33.0.42.15
Luca	33.30.42.45
Ancona	36.40.42.30
Bononia	33.30.43.40
Rhauennæ	35.0.43.15
Farraria	34.10.43.50
Parma	32.30.43.50
Verona	34.0.44.25
Venice	35.30.44.45
Padua	35.0.44.45
Mantua	33.10.44.10
Vincentia	34.39.44.20
Cremona	32.45.44.20
Placentia	32.30.44.20
Myllan	31.45.44.15
Tortona	31.30 44.0
Genua	31.30.43.15
Taurinum	30.40.43.45
Niſa	29.30.42.40

Secusia	29.45.44.0	Ioleos	51 3 .39 15
Graffa	29.50.42.55	Demetrias	50.30.38.56
Albinga	30.40.42.55	Lariffa	51.20.38.50
Vercellæ	30.30.44.30	Thebæ Thebs	51.10.38 30
Nouaria	30.15.45.0	Arniffa	45.20.40.40
		Elima	45.40.39 40
		Amantia	46.0.39 40
		Albenopolis	46.0.41.0
		Europus	46.30.41.20
		Apfalus	46.20.41.5
		Parocopolis	48.40.41.40
		Amphipolis	50.0.41 30

A PERTICVLER DE-
scription of Grece, and firste
of Macedonia.

MACEDONIA.

Acedonia hathe on
the Northe parte
Thrasia & the hier
Misnia:on theWest, the Ve-
netian seas:on thesouth parts
Epirus and Achaia : On the
East the Seas called Egiũ Pe
lagus. The principall Cities,
& townes of it are Theffalo-
nica, now Salonica the seate
of the chiefe Bishoppe of the
Philippians, vnto whome S.
Paule wrot two Epistles, the
first from Athenis, the secode
from Laodicia the chiefe bi-
shopriche of Phrygia, where
also S. Paule preached the
Gospell.   49.50.41.0

Apollonia	45.6.40.10
Aulon	44.50.39.56
Bullis	45.0.39.45
Arethusa	50.10.41.0
Panormus	54.404.1.0
Hadrianopolis	50.55.40.55
Ampelus	51.15.40.30

Philippis à Cítye where the
great Alexander was born,
and from this Citie S.Paule
sent his second Epistle to the
Galatians.   50.45.41.45

Heraclia   47.40.41.30

EPIRVS VVHOSE
cheife places are

Nicopolis	47.30.38 30
Cafsiopa	47.0.38.45
Ambracia:larta.	48.8.38.20

ACHAIA, VVHOSE
chiefe places are

Athenæ sometime the foun-
taine and wellspringe of all
good letters, heare did Plato
and Aristotle teach, it is now
destroyed.   52.45.37.15

Megaris	52.15.37.30
Peloponesus, Morea.	51.10.37.30
Modonam.	48.30.26.0
Parnaffus, a mount.	50.20.38 0

Helicon the holy Hill of
the Musis, at the foote, wher-

of

of is à founteine of the Houe
of Pegasus fote. 51.0.37.45
Pythia, the place wher Apol
lo gaue Oracles. 50.30.37.45
Constantinople, somtime
à citie vnder the Christiã Em
pire, but nowe the chiefe seat
of Solymanus th'Emperor of
Turkes, which he wã. 1453.
56.0.43.5.

Corinthe, the Bishoppes seat
in Achaia. Hether sent S.
Paule two Epistles, the first
frõ Philippis, à citie in Ma
cedonie by Stephan, fortuna-
tus, & Achaicus: The se-
conde Epistle by Titus, &
Luke.   51.15.36.55
Stymphalus.   50.20.
    36.20

Thus endeth the perticuler description
of Europe.

R iij.   Aperti-

FRICA, which also in Greke is named Λιβύη is the second part & portion of th' Earth. And was first so called of Iupiters daughter bering that name. But Festus saith it came of the qualitie of th' Aere, in that coutrey, deriuing it of φρίκη, as who should say, Ἀφρικη, that is, without horrour of coldenes: other affirme that it toke name of Afer, one of the posteritie of Abraham, which ouercomyng his enemies, remained in this part. It beginneth at Gaditanum Fretum (à narrow streight cōming out of th' Ocean into the middle Earth Seas, & haue Spaine on the north shore, & the Mores on the South) And it doeth ende at the Egiptiã Seas. On the North it haue the middle Earth seas, on the south shore the great Ocean, on th' East the sea, which stretche almost to the middle earth seas.

Africke is diuided into two parts by the hyll Atlas, of whiche the lesser extendeth to the middle Earth seas: the greater part goeth beyond this hill vnto the south Oceã. The greater part of it is not inhabited for two causis: one is for th' extreme heat, being vnder the burning zone, the Sōne draweth all the moister of th' earth frō it, so that for want of water no man cã ther liue. The second is for the

innu-

innumerable multitude of venamous wormes, & wilde
beaſtes, which are naturally ennemies vnto mankinde.
As the Lion, the Olephant, the Tiger, & ſuch like. Alſo,
Dragons, Chrocodile, Cocatrice, & ſundry other venomous Wormes, in ſuche ſorte that th'inhabitauntes are
compelled to put on botes, for better auoiding their ſting,
& poiſon. The part that is inhabited, is frutful enough.
The people blacke, Sauage, Monſtrous, & rude: yet in
thoſe countries, cities, & townes where the Spaniardes,
Portugalles, Italians, & other do frequent, the people
are ſumwhat more ciuill, modeſt, & reaſonable. Diuers
alſo (yea right graue authors) make metion of certaine
deformed that dwell in Africk, as men with dogges heades, called Cynocephali, ſome with one eye & that in the
forehead, named Monoculi, others without heades, &
theyr face in the breaſt, with diuers ſuch like which I ſup
poſe rather fables then any truth. ff you deſire à longer
deſcoure Towching Africk, hir inhabitates, & como-
dities, read Strabo, in his 2. & 17. bokes. And alſo Plinius his 8. boke, with diuers other writers, which at large
do herof intreate, & now f will (folowing my order be-
gun) ſet out the notable regios (which Ptolomæus num-
breth to be 12.) with theyr chiefe Cities, Townes, hilles,
& riuers, with in Africke: & firſt we will begin with
Mauritania, which is diuided into Mauritania Tin-
gitana, & Mauritania Cæſarienſi.

OF THE PRINCIPAL PLACES IN
Tingitana or Barbarica Mauritania.

R iiij.   Feſ-

Fesse 10.0.30.0

Tingis cæfaria called commenlye
Tanger 6.30.35.30

Abilis one of Hercules Pillers, is a
hill againfte Calpe an other Hill
in Spaine 7.50.35.40

Baba 8.10.34.20

Banafa 6.30.34.20

Septa 7.30.35.55

Sala 6.55.34.0

The Sonnes Mount 6.45.31.15

Benta 9.30.33.40

Dorath. 10.10.31.15

Tamufida 7.15.34.15

MAVRITANIA CÆ-farienfis.

Apollos promontorie 15.30.33.40

Iulia Cæfaria. 17.0.33.20

Tucca. 20.0.31.30

Hippa. 20.15.29.50

La Guardia. 12.0.34.20

Ciffa. Cerlel. 18.45.32.10

IN AFRICK THE leffe.

Colops the greater. 27.40.32.20

Colops the leffer. 29.20.32.35

Hippon 30.30.32.15

Utica, where Cato died, now called Benfert. 32.0.32.45.

Carthage. 34.40.31.50

Clupea. 35.0.33.20

Sabatra. 41.0.31.0

Vfanum. 33.15.32.20

Dabia 33.0.29.40

NVMIDIA.

Culuca 28.30.31.0

Tucca 29.30.31.20

Bizancina 37.50.30.40

Capfa. 37.30.29.45

Calatha. 31.0.53.40

Sabrata 41.15.30.50

Ammon. 65.30.28.0

Oafsis the great. 59.20.26.55

MARMARICA.

Alexandria. 60.30.31.0

Memphis 62.50.29.50

Cayrum 62.15.30.0

Syëne. 62.15.23.50

LYBIA INTERIOR.

Tagaza 7.0.15.40

Tuchorora. 12.30.16.0

Tambutum 15.30.15.40

MEROE.

Meroë is an Flåd of Nilus, fometime called Saba, & now Elfaba, where S. Matthew did preache the Gofpel. From hence came the quene of Saba, to here Salomõs wifdome. From hence alfo came Cãdaces, the quenes Enuche, which was baptifed of Philip th' Appoftle. But at this prefēt it is the feate of the mightie prince, that we cal Preter John. 61.30.16.25

QVIOLA.

Quiola, or Cayla, is à region, in which great plentie of Cinamome growe, the chiefe cities are

Hamaharica. 65.0.9.10

Mafta. 67.30. South Pole. 4.1.

Beritis. 60.40.21.31

Quiola. 76.30. South pole. 7.30

Sabath. 67.30.12.30

Mombaza. 79.0. South Pole. 6.0.

Melinda. 82.30.2.0

Ca-

Cauaquin. 80.0.9.50

Babell mendap. There are the ſtreightes of the red ſeas.
74.50.11.0.

OF CITIES OF SON=
dry Regions, in Southe Æthiopia.

Goia 60.50.   South Pole.19.50
Garma.57.0   South Pole. 24.0
Bali   70.0.21.40
Meli   33.0.16.30

OF THE NOTABLE
Ilandes about Africke.

Porto Sancto.   0.35.31.30

Medera an Flande, firſte inhabited of the Portugales,

it aboūdeth with Suger, Honie, Wax, & ſundrye Herbes.   358.40.29.50

The Canarian Flādes beyng x. in numbre.   1.30.23.30

S. Thomas Flād. 32.30.0.30

Madagaſcar, whiche is alſo called Saint Laurence Ilād, there the North Pole is not ſene, & the nedle in ſailynge will do no ſeruice. Therefore they ar cōſtreined to vſe Aſtrolabes, & other Inſtrumēts.
85.30. South Pole. 20.0,

Thus endeth the Deſcription of Africke.

OF

Fol.190   THE FIFTH BOOKE OF THE
OF ASIA THE THIRDE
parte of th'Earth.

HAT *Asia* is, and wherof it was firste so called, there is no controuersie. For all writers, as wel Historiographers, as also Geographers, make it the iij. part of th'Earth, & to take that name of *Asius*, sonne to kinge *Cotis*. And although they call it the iij. part of th'Earth, yet it is not because it conteyneth but the thirde part, but bycause it is so diuided by the seas, for of it selfe it is as much as Europe, & *Africke*, & conteineth (after *Ptolomæus* accompt) 48. Prouinces. It is parted into *Asia* the greater, & *Asia* the lesser. Notwithstandyng diuers wryters vse this worde *Asia* the lesser, more largelye than Geographers doth. For they call all that portiō which is within the south shore of the ponticke seas, & th'east seas *Pelagus Ægeum*, & the North part of our Ocean, & the West part of the Riuer *Euphrates* to be *Asia* the lesser. *Asia* conteyneth in hir circuit, *Bythinia Pōtus*, the lesser *Asia*, *Lycia*, *Galatia*, *Paphlagonia*, *Pāphilia*, *Capadocia*, the lesser *Armenia*, & *Cilicia*. And all these after the maner of th'olde Grecians, is comprehended within this one word Ἀνατολία *Anatolia*, that is to say th'east plage or coaste. *Asia* dothe farre excell both Europe and *Africke*.

Africke. For it is so frutefull, hathe so pleasaunt sildes, such plētie of foder & pasture, the heauens geuing moisture to th'Earth in due season. It hath aboūdāce of golde mines. It bringeth forthe plentie of Cinamome, Ginger, Aloës, & diuers aromaticall spices, & Gūmes. There are diuerse straunge beastes bred in Asia, as Vnicornes, Camelles, Liberdes, Mermosites, Mercattes, Grippes. Yet one thing is to them infortunate, that there are terrible & many Earthquakes, in so much that there haue bene x. & xij. Cities at one time subuerted, & ouerthrowen. Th'inhabitauntes are sundrye, & diuers: for some are Anthropophagi, which eate thē flesh of men:& drinke their bloud. Ther are also Pygmeans (men but à cubite in height) which riding on Goates, & Rāmes, do kepe warre with Cranes. Ther ar diuers other formes of inhabitauntes resited of Plinius, whiche at this present J willingly ouerpasse. The spirites in this coūtrie, by many illusions seke to bringe trauailers into daungers, sumtime by calling them by theyr names, other times by musicall noise, as it were alluringe thē by the swetnes of the sounde, vntil they be brought into danger through wilde beastes. But now these thinges omitted, (whiche would make à great volume of them selues) I will briefely set out the chiefe & principall places of Asia, beginnynge with Pontus, & Bythinia.

PONTVS AND
Bythinia.

Chalcedon.	56.20.43.5	
Olbia.	57.0.42.40	
Nicodemia	56.0.42.40	

Claudiopolis, where S. Luke did write his Gospell, & the Actes

Actes of th' Apostles.59.30.
42.45.

Nicæa, where the Nicene
counsell was.   58.0.42.15

Cæsaria, smirdiana. 56.40.41.40

Olimpus, an Hill of whiche
I spake in the first boke.
57.0.41.40.

THESE FOLOVVINGE
are properly called Cities
of Asia.

Lampsacus.	55.20.41.25

Illium, somtime called Troie
now Ruinous.   55.50.41.0

Dardanū,Dardanellū.	55.25.40.5.
Alexandria.	55.25.40.40
Autandrus.	56.30.40.20

Smyrna, the coūtrey where
Homer was borne. 58.25.38.
25.

Assum.	56.30.40.15

Ephesus, the chiefe citie
in Ionia, in whiche S. Iohn
wrot his gospel.57.40.3740

CITIES OF CARIA.

Heraclea.	58.50.43.30
Miletus	58.0.37.0
Nysa	59.0.38.15
Antiochia.	59.30.38.20
Neapolis.	59.25.38.35

Trallis, which is also called
Emāthia, at which place cer
teine suppose Pygmeans inhabit.   58.40.38.5

OF BOTH LYDIAS

Philadelphia	59.0.38.50
Sardis	58.20.28.15
Sala	60.15.38.20
Sanis	61.0.38.20
Hierapolis	55.20.38.15
Apamia	55.30.42.0

CITIES OF LYCAO-
nia or Lycia.

Carya	59.50.35.55
Patara	60.30.36.0
Olimpus a Citie	61.30.36.10
Xanthus,Patara	60.30.36.40
Migra	61.0.36.45

CITIES OF GALA-
tia.

Sinopa stala	63.30.43.0

Pompeiopolis so called because Pompey builded it.
62.0.42.0

Claudiopolis	63.15.42.20
Ancyra	62.40.42.0
Laodicæa	60.15.38.40

OF PAMPHILIA.

Olbia	62.0.36.55
Magydis	62.40.36.55
Seleusia	62.0.38.30
Antiochia	62.30.39.0

CITIES OF DORIS.

Alicarnassus	57.50.36.10
Cadmos an hill	59.40.37.40
Phenix an hill	58.0.36.30
Apollonia	57.0.39.45

Pargamus, here was the noble Physicion Galenus born,
whiche made Phisicke per-
faite, and expoundes Hippo-
crates.57.35.39.45.

CAPADOCIA.

Tra-

Trapezus Genech.   68.50.43.5
Sebastopolis.s. Greg. 66.0 41.20.
Zama.   65.0.40.45
Archelais.   64.45.39.40

Cæsaria. Maza, here was Basilius magnus Bishoppe. 66.30.39.30

Derba.   64.30.38.15

OF ARMENIA THE lesser.

Satala.   96.50.42.10
Nicopolis.   69.20.41.40
Ispa.   70.30.40.20
Camana.   68.0.38 0
Claudia.   71.0.38,45

CILICIA.

Antiochia   64.40.36.50
Agææ   69.0.36,30
Seleucia   66 10.36.45
Tarsos.S.Paules countrie. 67.40.36.50
Epiphania   69.30.36,0

OF COLCHIS.

Neapolis. Negapotimo. 71.30.45.40.
Geapolis   72.0.45.30
Phasis   72.30.45.0.
Madia   74.15.46.15

OF IBERIA.

Sura   75.0.45.20.
Zalissa   76.0.44.40
Varica.   75.20.46.0

ALBANIA PART of great Tertarye.

Gelda.   83.0.46.30
Albana,   81.40.45.50
Bacchia.   77.0.44.40
Baruca.   79.20.44.40

ARMENIA THE greater.

Lala.   76.10.44.0
Brizaca   74.50.45.30
Babila.   73.15.40.45

Anarium.   76.50.41.30
Belcania.   73.50.39.40

OF SYRIA, THE CITIES

Alexandria   69.30.36.10
Selutia   67.30.32.50
Laodicea,Ramatha   88.30.35.3
Posidium   88.30.35.15
Myriandrus. Alapso   69.30.35.50

PHÆNICIA.

Tripolis   67.30,34.20
Biblus   67.40.33.55
Sidon   67 30.33.30
Tyrus   67.5.33.18

Sor, comenly called Sur, à citie after the ruine of Alexã der christened: now destroied of the Turk. Of the ij. cities, Sidõ & Tyrus, Christ our sauior in his gospel speketh.

Ptolomais,Acon.   66.50,33.0

Berytus, but of our trauellers nowe called Barut, it is the Port of Damascus. 67.0. 33.20.

Botrys,Botrus.   67.50.34.5
Dora.   66.30.32.40

Antiochia nye the moũt Taurus, the Countrey of S. Luke Euangelist. 69.0.35.30

Laonia.   70.30.36.20

OF CVRVA, THE CISIES.

Abila Lysanium.   68.45 33.20

Damascus, here did Cain, sle his brother Abel. 69.0.33.0

Adra.   68.40.32.10
Hippus,Sephet.   68.0.32.30

S.i.   Capi-

Capitolia Suueta   69.45.32.30
Philadelphia   68.0.31.20

LAODICINA.

Paradissus   69.45.33.35

IVDEA OR PALE-
stina.

Ioppa, Ioppen or Iaffa à port whiche was builded before the diludge. 65.45.31.55

Ascalon, hibelis commonly called Escolona. 65.0.31.40

The dead seas or lake of Sodome. 66.50.31.10

OF GALILÆA.

Iulias or Bethsaida, the coū-try of s.Peter, & s.Andrew. 67.5.31.15.

OF SAMARIA.

Neapolis, Sichen here did Christe conuerte the Samaritane. 66.50.31.50

IVDVA.

Gaza   65.25.31.15
Sebasta, Samaria   65.40.31.30
Lydda.Rama   66.0.32.0
Ericus, Ierico   66 15.31.25

Nicopolis sumtime called Emaus, here was Christe knowne by breaking of bread 65.45.31.50.

Ierusalem which is now called Capitolia: & haue diuers

other names: here was our sauiour Christ Iesus crucified, & paid the raunsome for our sinnes in the beginning of the 34.yeare of his bodelye age. 65.45.31.22.

IDVMÆA.

Berzamma   64.50.31.15
Maps.Massa   65.40 30.50

MESOPOTAMIA.

Porsica   72.0.37.30
Soleucia Mosell   79.0.35.40
Edesse.Rase   72.30.37.30
Zama   75.20.36.30

Carre, Charan, here did the holye Patriarch, Abraham dwell. 73.45.36.10.

Babilon, Baldach the chiefe Bishops sea in Chadea here (building the tower Babel) spräg the cöfusion of tonges. 79.0.35.0.

Bilba   79.0.35.0
Cesa   76.40.32.50
Thelma   77.40.32.0
Orchoë   78 30.32.40

ARABIA VVHICHE IS
parted in thre parts: Arabia deserta, Petrea, & Felix.

Frupa   72 30.30.15
Sora   75.0.30.20
Choca   72.3 .32.40
Salma   78.2 .29.20
Lysa   65.50.30 15
Petra   66.45.30.20.
Lydia   69.0.30.40

The red seas through which

Moses

Moses, & th'Israelites went
63.30.29.50.

Adra   63.40.31.40

Mout Sinay, which is also called the mounte Oreb, or Choreb. Here receiued Moses the x. comaundementes.
64.0 30.0.

Thebæ	69.40.21.0
Muza	74.30.14.0
Sanina	75.30.11.30
Arabia.Aden	80.0.11.30
Moscha	88.30.14.0
Cabana	85.0.23.0
Istriona	80.0.25.40
Badea.Gydda	70.0.20.15

Mecha. Here is the Sepulcher of Mahomet, which the Turkes go to visite wyth great deuotion, & yet straungers comyng thether se no other thing thē à golden shoe, hanginge in the rouffe of the Temple.   72.15.23.0

Saba, the seate of Gaspar the king, which broughte golde of Arabie, to offer vnto Jesus, beyng à Childe.   76.0.13.0

ASSIRIA.

Ninus, Niniuie, à great Citie, but nowe desolate vnto whiche Jonas the Prophete

was sent.   78,0.36.0

Cteliphon	80.0.35.0
Arbila	80.0.37.15

MEDIA.

Zalaca	86.15.41.0
Mandagara	87.45.39.30
Ecbatana	88.0.37.45
Veneca	93.20.38.15
Gariauna	91.0.37.20
Trauaxa	92.0.37.40
Rapsa	90.10.35.40
Aradripha	93.20.34.45

SVSANA.

Asia a Citie.	80.10.31 40
Susa Sambragata	84.0.34.15
Tariana	84.0.32.30
Agra	80.30.33.45

PERSIA.

Axima	87.45.33.50
Persipolis	90.0.35.10
Diodorus	91.0.33.20
Niserga	90.15.34.0
Tragonica	87.40.32.40
Bassara	81.20.29.50

CARMANIA.

Agris	96.30.23.0
Gerniana	100.0.29.0
Thaspis	98.0.27.40
Armusa	94.30.23.30

PARTHIA.

Hecatompylon, à City which haue an hundreth gates.
96.20.37.50.

Rhoara	98.30.38.20
Ambrodax	94.30.38.20
Rhagæa	98.20.34.20
Appha.	98.0.35.20

HIRCANIA.

Hercana	98.30.40.0
Adrapsa	98.30.41.40

Saca   94.15.39.30

MARGIANA.

Sena   102.30.42.20
Iasonium   103 30.41.30
Antiochia margiana 106.0 41.40
Nigæa   105.0.41.10

BACTRIANA.

Chomara   106.302.4.40
Menapia   113.0.41.20
Bactra   116.0.41.0

SOGDIANA.

Prepsa   130.0.45.0
Alexandria oxiana   113.0.44.40

Scythia within the Mounte Emaus.

Aspabota   102.0.44.0
Dauaba   104.0.45.0
Scithia without the mount Emaus.

The kingdome of Chatay is vnder the greatCham, king of the Tartarians, the chiefe Cities are

Iſſedon ſcithica   150.0.48.30
Soeta   145.0.35.20

SERICA.

Iſſedon ſerica   162.0.45.0
Sera   177.15.38.35
Dama   156.0.51.40

In this country breed the Wormes which make ſilk, we call them in Engliſhe Silke Wormes, of which at this day the Spaniardes haue greate Plentye.

ARIA AND ARIANA.
The middes of it   106.0.35.30
Namaris   105.40.36.10

Articaudna   109.20.36 10
Alexandria Ariæ   110.0.36.0

DRANGIANA.

Afta   107.30.30.40
Bigis   111.0.29.20
Agriapſa   108.0.34.0

GEGROSIA.

Cumi   110.0.23.50
Parſis   106.30.23.30
Arbis   105.20.20.30

INDIA VVITH IN
the riuer Ganges.

Bardaxima   213.40.20.40
Monogloſſum   114.10.18.20
Mandagara   113.0.14.30
Nitria   115.10.14.20

Colchi now called Cuchina, vnto which the Lucitanians are very frendly 123.0.15.0
Salur   125.0.15.0
Bizantium   113.40.14.40
Tyndis   138.30 16.10

Calicutium, Calechut. The moſte famous Citie of Marchaundiſe in all India, they haue à proper Kinge of their owne : but the Crowne come not by ſucceſſion vnto theyr children for this cauſe. For they haue thys vſe that whan any manne marieth, he muſt commit his wife to the prieſt to be defloured. Vnto this city is brought frõ all India al kind

of

of ſpice, Cloues, Nutmegges
Giger, Cinamome, Rubarbe,
Muſk, Săders, Aloës, Caſſia.
Alſo præcious ſtones of diuers
kindes, & al maner of ſilkes.
Ther ar diuerſe ſortes of inhabitantes in this citie: Chri-
ſtians, Turkes, Mahomites,
Caſſranans, Idolaters. And
this laſt kinde do often (as it
ware in token of Frendſhip)
lend theyr wiues one to another   .112.0.5.0

Simylla	110.0.14.45
Hippocura	120.30.4.0
Caticardama, Corimandel.	136.
20.12.40	
Sambolaca	132.15,31.50

PRASIA.

Palibotra	143.0.27.0
Tamalitis	144.30.16.30
Sambalaca	141.0.29.30

COVNTRIES AND CI-
ties without Ganges in India.

Pentapolis	150.0.18.0
Baracura. Bangella	152.30 16.0
Sabara	159.0.8.30
Begynga	162.20.8.26
Tacola	160.30.4.15
Sabana	160.0.3.0
Colipolis	164.20.0.0
Balonga	167.30.7.0
Synda	167.15.13.40
Thagora	168.0.6.0

Eldana, hither came S.

Thomas to præche the Goſ-
pell.   152.0.13.0

Trygliphon	154.0.17.0
Gorgatha	167.0.12.30

CHATAY, A REGION.

Chataio	222.0.43.50
VVeaſt Ciamſu	222.0.37.17

Quinſay, the greateſt Ci-
tie in all th'Earthe, and is as
muche to ſaye with vs, as the
heauenly Citie, in the middes
of it, is a Lake, whiche in the
circuit, haue 1200. Bridges.
226.0.37.40.

Geiten	259.0.25.15
Eaſt Ciamſu	231.0.32.5
Focho	240.55.7.0
Tingrei	236.0.35.0

MANGI, THIS CON-
teine in it. 9. kingdomes.

Taygni	224.15.31.0
Sygni	232.0.29.20

Thebet, a Prouince in which
the great Cham, lorde of the
Eaſt, & ſouth Indians haue
his ſeate, & all the kinges of
India are vnder him.   204.
10.3.20.

CYAMBA.

Cyamba   208.10.25 30

Theſe vſe Corall in the

steade of money, they haue great plentie of Nutmegges, Aloës, & all kinde of Spices.

SOVTH INDIA.

Th'inhabitantes are all Idolaters, & haue thefe kingdomes folowyng.

Lamia	202.10.11.40
Morfuli	285.0.13.0
Thime	180.0.

South Pole.3.10.

MOABAR.

Nar. The inhabitantes do worship Oxen　276.0. South Pole.20.10 Malaqua, here was S. Thomas flain 260.6.　　　South Pole.15 30

THE KINGDOME
of Lac.

_Lac, à citie, th'inhabitã-tes worfhip Oxē, & ar great Idolaters, yet iuft in their affaires, & haters of lyes, & liers._166.30.21.40.

¶ OF THE ILANDES adiacent to Afia, and India, and newe Regions of this iij. part lately founde oute.

CYPRVS.

IT is an Iflande in the middle earth Seas, in which Iaphat, one of Noë his fonnes, firft inhabitid.　65.30.35.10

SCOTORA.

Scotora, in Arabie the happie now it is called Scoyra. 86.20.12.0.

ORMVSA.

Ormufa is an Iflãd in the narrow Perfick feas. 96.20 19.0

TABROBANA.

_It is alfo named Samotra, it is à great Ilande._151.15. _It is without Latitude, becaufe it is vnder th'Equinoctiall._

COO.

Coo, an Ilande, in whiche the the prince of Phyfitians Hippocrat. was born. 57.0.36.25

THE GREATER
Iaua.

Iaua.　179.0. the fouth pole .7.30

BORNO.

_Borno, an Ilande._178.0. The South pole.2.30

THE LESSER
Iaua.

_Iaua._188.9. _Vnder th'equinoctiall._

AMBICON.

Ambicon.166.0.　The fouth pole 7.0.

GELILO.

Gelilo, alfo Solor, one of the greateft Ilandes of Moluck. 204.0.　　The fouth Pole..1.0

Iflandes

ILANDES OF
Moluck.

It is vnder the Tropicke of
Cancer.

Th'other Jlandes are vnder
193.0.9.0.digrees.

IAMAICA.

IVCATAN
Iucatan.   257.30.19.0

Iamaica.   270 0.19.
30.

CVBA.
Cuba.   269.30.23.30

VASANDREA.
Vasandrea.   331.30.
40.0.

❧Thus endeth the perticuler description
of Asia.

S iiij.   APER.

A PERTICVLER DESCRIPTION OF
*suche partes of America, as are by trauaile
founde out.*

*IGHT ordèr inforseth that (the iij. partes of the Earth, beynge set out accordynge to their notable partes) I shall direct my Penne to speake of America, whiche is named the fourth parte, & was to Ptolomæus, & th'Auncient Geographers vnknowē: as also at this præsent great part of it is not yet foūd out. It taketh the name of America, of Americus Vesputius, who by the cōmaundement of Ferdinando king of Castell, founde it out, in the yeare of Christ oure Sauiour. 1497. aboute th'ende of June, as doeth appeare by his owne testimonie. The people bothe men, & women are naked, neither suffer they any heare to growe on their bodies, no not on their browes, the head except. They are excellent in swiming, both men & women, so that they without werines can swime ij. leaques. Their weapons are bowes, & arrowes, which they præpare, & head with stones, & the teath of Fishe, for that they want Iron, & all metall (gold except.) They haue warre with th'inhabitauntes of the countrey next them, which haue an other language. But it is not for richesse, for inlarging their segniory, or election of à king : but for to reuenge the deathes of their prædicessors. There is no
lawe*

law or order obſerued of wedlocke, for it is lawful to haue
ſo many wemen as they affeſt, & to put them away with
out any daunger. They be filthy at meate, & in all ſe-
crete aſtes of nature, comparable to brute beaſtes. Their
bread is rotes, & theyr meate mans fleſhe, for all theyr
enemies, which they ouercome, they with great banket-
tyng deuoure. Their houſes are builded like the ſhape of
Belles, & couered with leaues & palmes of trees. they
vſe no kinde of Marchandiſe, and as for golde, Pearle,
ſtone, & that we haue in great priſe: they haue in no eſti
mation. For theyr richeſſe is in fethers of diuers colours,
& ſtones, which they hange on their eares & lips for an
ornatur. They do honour the Sonne, Mone, & Sterres.
There is alſo in the weaſt part of America, à region cal
led Peru, moſt riche of all other that hitherto haue bene
founde both of meatalles, & præcious Drugges. Their
ſhepe be of ſuche fertilitie, that they twiſe yearlye haue
Lambe. Th'inhabitantes are ciuill, wiſe, prudẽt, ſkilful
of marchandiſe. But yet they know not Chriſt. The middes of America is in digrees. 330.0. The pole Antarſtik
10.0. The breadth of it is 2100. Engliſh miles, the lẽgth
3000. miles. There are diuers and ſundry Ilandes about
America, in our dayes founde oute of whiche hereafter
ſhall folow the principall.

PERV VVITH THE
ſhore towarde Spaine.

Peru.	290.5.0.ſouth pole.	
Archay Cherſoneſus.	303.0.5.0	
Caput de Stado.	317.0.2.30	

Sinus aquæ dulcis, here
are vij. Ilandes founde, in
which are great plentie of
Pearle, & præcious Sto-
nes.

nes.   322.0. *South Pole.* 5.0.
Rio grande 329.0. South pole. 4.30
S. Rochi   341.0. South pole. 8.15
Caput S. Crucis, here Mage-
lanus founde à Giaunt x. fote
in length. 345.0.14.0.
Rio. s. Iacobi   356.0.23.30
Rio de. s. Lucia   341.0.27.20
ILANDES ADIOY-
ning to America.
Riqua the leſſer   296.0.10.0
Riqua the greater   300.0.9.0
Th'Iland of Giants   308.7.5.0
Th'Ilande of Braſil   305.4.6.10
La ponto   318.30.4.0

Spagnolla, here is found, Gua
iacū that healeth the Nea-
politane ſicknes.   *And the*
middes of th'Flande cōteine.
305.0.23.0.
¶ILANDES TOVVARD
Africke, are innumerable of
whiche theſe are founde
oute.
Todoſanctos   332.30.17.0
Deſorana   323.0.18.0
Degadalupo   331.10.15.30
Caput de bonauentur 294.10.4.10
The grene Iland.   347.0.14.0

FINIS.

A PLENTIFVL TABLE CONTEYNING

the principall matters of the whole worke, reduced in=
to th'ordor of th'Alphabete, for the spedier findynge of
suche thinges, as you require.

T ii.

FINIS.

Faultes escaped in the Imprinting.

Fol. 2. the vi. lyne, Ingens, reade Engeins.

Fol. 25. th'eightene lyne, goeth ouerthwart them, read, goeth ouerthwart the
  Sphere.

Fol. 69. the xxi. lyne, Zolstitii, reade Solstitii.

Fol. 121. the last lyne, whose compasse, read whose compositiō is in this wise. Describe a Circle with your compasse.

Fol. 189. the ii. columbe, the last lyne, it exten- reade, it extendeth.

¶ AN EXTRACTE OF THE QVENES

highnes gracious Priuiledge, & Licence.

ELIZABETH by the grace of God Quene of Englande, Fraunce, and Ire=lande, defendour of the faith &c.

To all maner of Printers, Booke fel=lers, and other our Officers, Minifters, and fubiectes: greatyng. VVe do you to vnderftand, that of our grace efpeciall, we haue graunted, & geuen priuiledge and licence: And by thefe prefentes for vs, our heyres, and fucceffors do graunt and gyue Priuiledge and Lycence, vnto our welbeloued fubiect Iohn Day, of the citie of London, Printer, and Stationer, and to his affi=gnes for the terme of his life, to Imprint, or caufe to be Imprinted, as well the Cofmographicall Glaffe, compiled by VVilliam Cuningham Doctor in Phyficke, as alfo durynge the tyme of vij. yeares, all fuche Bookes, and workes, as he hath Imprinted, or herafter fhall Imprint, being diuifed, compiled, or fet out by any learned man, at the procure=ment, coftes, & charge, only of the faid Iohn Day. Straitly forbiddyng and commaunding by thefe prefentes, all and finguler our fubiectes, as well Printers, & Bookefellers, as all other perfons within our Real=mes & Dominions, what fo euer they be, in any maner of wife, to Im=print, or caufe to be Imprinted, any of the aforefaid Bookes, that the faid Iohn Day fhall by authoritie of this our licence, imprint, or caufe to be imprinted, or any part of them: But onely the faid Iohn Day, and his affignes, vpon payne of our hyghe indignation. And that euery of=fendor therin fhall forfaite to our vfe fourtie fhillinges of lawfull mo=ney of Englande, for euery fuch Book or Bookes, at any time fo Prin=ted contrary to the true meanyng of this oure prefent Licence, and Priuiledge: Ouer and befides all fuche Booke, or Bookes fo Printed, to be forfayted to whom fo euer fhall fuftayne the charges, & fue the fayd forfaiture in our behalfe. &c.

Geuen at our Palice of VVeftminfter the xxviii. day of Octo-ber, the firfte yeare of our Reigne.

¶ Imprinted at London by
*John Day, dwellyng ouer Aldersgate, be-
neath Saint Martins.*
1559.